Solutio...
the Healthcare
Quality Crisis

Also available from ASQ Quality Press:

Lean-Six Sigma for Healthcare: A Senior Leader Guide to Improving Cost and Throughput, Second Edition
Greg Butler, Chip Caldwell, and Nancy Poston

The Public Health Quality Improvement Handbook
Ron Bialek, Grace L. Duffy, and John W. Moran, editors

Lean Six Sigma for the Healthcare Practice: A Pocket Guide
Roderick A. Munro

A Lean Guide to Transforming Healthcare: How to Implement Lean Principles in Hospitals, Medical Offices, Clinics, and Other Healthcare Organizations
Thomas G. Zidel

Improving Healthcare Using Toyota Lean Production Methods: 46 Steps for Improvement, Second Edition
Robert Chalice

On Becoming Exceptional: SSM Health Care's Journey to Baldrige and Beyond
Sister Mary Jean Ryan, FSM

Journey to Excellence: Baldrige Health Care Leaders Speak Out
Kathleen Goonan, Joseph A. Muzikowski, and Patricia K. Stoltz, editors

Benchmarking for Hospitals: Achieving Best-in-Class Performance without Having to Reinvent the Wheel
Victor Sower, Jo Ann Duffy, and Gerald Kohers

The Certified Six Sigma Green Belt Handbook
Roderick A. Munro, Matthew J. Maio, Mohamed B. Nawaz, Govindarajan Ramu, and Daniel J. Zrymiak

Six Sigma for the New Millennium: A CSSBB Guidebook, Second Edition
Kim H. Pries

The Certified Six Sigma Black Belt Handbook, Second Edition
T. M. Kubiak and Donald W. Benbow

5S for Service Organizations and Offices: A Lean Look at Improvements
Debashis Sarkar

To request a complimentary catalog of ASQ Quality Press publications, call 800-248-1946, or visit our Web site at http://www.asq.org/quality-press.

Solutions to the Healthcare Quality Crisis

Cases and Examples of Lean Six Sigma in Healthcare

Søren Bisgaard, Editor

The work on this book has been generously supported
by the Eugene and Ronnie Isenberg Endowment.

ASQ Quality Press
Milwaukee, Wisconsin

American Society for Quality, Quality Press, Milwaukee 53203
© 2009 by ASQ
All rights reserved. Published 2009
Printed in the United States of America
15 14 13 12 11 10 09   5 4 3 2 1

Library of Congress Cataloging-in-Publication Data

Solutions to the healthcare quality crisis : cases and examples of lean six sigma in healthcare / Søren Bisgaard, editor.
   p. cm.
   Includes bibliographical references and index.
   ISBN 978-0-87389-769-3 (soft cover : alk. paper)
   1. Health services administration—Quality control. 2. Six sigma (Quality control standard) I. Bisgaard, Søren, 1951-

   RA399.A3S58 2009
   362.1068—dc22   2009013276

ISBN: 978-0-87389-769-3

Publisher: William A. Tony
Acquisitions Editor: Matt T. Meinholz
Project Editor: Paul O'Mara
Production Administrator: Randall Benson

ASQ Mission: The American Society for Quality advances individual, organizational, and community excellence worldwide through learning, quality improvement, and knowledge exchange.

Attention Bookstores, Wholesalers, Schools, and Corporations: ASQ Quality Press books, videotapes, audiotapes, and software are available at quantity discounts with bulk purchases for business, educational, or instructional use. For information, please contact ASQ Quality Press at 800-248-1946, or write to ASQ Quality Press, P.O. Box 3005, Milwaukee, WI 53201-3005.

To place orders or to request a free copy of the ASQ Quality Press Publications Catalog, including ASQ membership information, call 800-248-1946. Visit our Web site at www.asq.org or http://www.asq.org/quality-press.

Printed in the United States of America

 Printed on acid-free paper

Quality Press
600 N. Plankinton Avenue
Milwaukee, Wisconsin 53203
Call toll free 800-248-1946
Fax 414-272-1734
www.asq.org
http://www.asq.org/quality-press
http://standardsgroup.asq.org
E-mail: authors@asq.org

Table of Contents

Part II: Cases and Examples of the Use of Lean Six Sigma in Healthcare

List of Figures and Tables

Taking Performance to a Higher Level

Engaging Physicians in Lean Six Sigma

Learning from Mistakes

Hospital Reduces Medication Errors Using DMAIC and QFD

Faster Turnaround Time

Lean Six Sigma Reduces Medication Errors

Quality Intervenes at a Hospital

Toward Error-Free Lab Work

Healthcare Department Reduces Cycle Time and Errors

Preface

WHAT IS THE PURPOSE OF THIS BOOK?

Healthcare around the world is in crisis as a result of complex structural and strategic problems that will require solutions at a very high level. Notwithstanding these larger issues, this book demonstrates that effective solutions based on modern quality management principles can be applied locally to alleviate many problems within healthcare institutions.

Accordingly, this book is designed to support doctors, nurses, technicians, and administrators who are interested in applying quality management principles and the tools of Lean Six Sigma to improve healthcare within their own institutions. The book should also be of interest to politicians, policy makers, and government officials wrestling with healthcare issues.

WHY THIS BOOK?

Decision makers often "believe" that there is a necessary trade-off between quality and cost of healthcare. This book provides evidence to the contrary.

The application of Lean Six Sigma to healthcare can provide effective solutions to chronic quality problems. Benefits include:

- Improved patient care while saving or freeing up resources and improving top- and bottom-line results

- Improved management systems, administration, and related services that prevent problems and errors and facilitate better and cheaper healthcare

- More effective use of knowledge and ideas already resident in healthcare providers

- Empowered employees making changes that benefit patients and the institution

- More constructive cross-functional relations and communication that strengthen and enhance the culture of the entire organization

- Methods and capabilities that will be invaluable as high-level solutions and public policies are adopted

Healthcare professionals can assume leadership within their own institutions by applying quality management principles and proven approaches to quality improvement. They can start quality improvement programs now—even while the public policy debates continue. The cases in this book show how.

WHAT DOES THIS BOOK DELIVER?

This book delivers:

- An overview of key quality management principles and Lean Six Sigma methods, tools, and techniques, including how to apply them to healthcare

- A frank discussion of perils and pitfalls of misapplication of quality management principles

- Case studies that show step-by-step successful projects with lessons learned

- Examples of effective and practical solutions to chronic quality problems from all areas of healthcare, patient care, and administration, without waiting for resolution of the worldwide healthcare crisis

CAN WE REDUCE THE COST AND IMPROVE THE QUALITY OF HEALTHCARE AT THE SAME TIME?

Most people believe there is a necessary trade-off between quality and cost. To cut the rising costs of healthcare, they believe, we must be prepared to compromise our quality requirements. But that is not necessarily so! Reducing costs while improving quality is not a contradiction! The cost of poor quality and the unnecessary waste in current healthcare delivery systems are significant drivers of the escalating costs of healthcare in the United States. *Making mistakes and having to fix them is expensive!* This book provides numerous examples of healthcare professionals taking initiatives that improved quality *and* reduced cost.

Many chronic quality problems in healthcare delivery systems, as exemplified in this book, can be significantly reduced or eliminated by using simple systematic and evidence-based approaches to quality improvement. The goal should always be to develop solutions that prevent quality problems from occurring in the first place. As Dr. W. Edwards Deming once joked about toasting bread, "First we burn it, and then we scrape it." Would it not be better and cheaper to adjust the toaster to prevent the bread from getting burned in the first place?

WHO IS THIS BOOK WRITTEN FOR?

This book is specifically intended for healthcare professionals with no previous background, knowledge, or experience with Lean Six Sigma. More broadly, it should be of interest to anyone interested in healthcare quality—doctors, nurses, pharmacists, technicians, healthcare administrators, consultants, concerned citizens, politicians, policy analysts, government officials, and so on. In the book you will find a number of cases from American and European healthcare organizations of the use of Lean Six Sigma, documented by pioneering frontline healthcare professionals including doctors, nurses, and healthcare administrators—willing to take personal responsibility and show leadership—who were doing something to improve quality and reduce the escalating costs of healthcare.

Lean Six Sigma is a powerful approach to quality improvement originally developed for improving quality and reducing waste in the manufacturing industry. With appropriate modifications, this approach has been shown to be very effective in improving quality in healthcare as well. This book provides numerous examples that demonstrate that it is indeed possible to improve quality while reducing costs.

A BOOK FOR DOERS!

This book is not about theory. It is a book for doers—healthcare providers—about how to do it. This is a book that shows healthcare professionals how they can take their destiny in their own hands and do something about healthcare quality and costs. It is a book of cases showing how quality was improved, and demonstrating to others how they can do the same. The book presents a wide selection of examples of the applications of Lean Six Sigma originally published in two of the American Society for Quality's journals—*Quality Progress* and *Six Sigma Forum Magazine*—over the past few years. Each case illustrates some aspect of how to improve quality and reduce waste in healthcare institutions whether in the direct delivery of healthcare or on the equally important administrative side. Some of the cases are from large metropolitan hospitals and others are from smaller institutions. Most of the cases show what has worked, while a few show pitfalls or obstacles to be avoided.

EVIDENCE-BASED QUALITY IMPROVEMENT

The Lean Six Sigma methodology is very well suited to healthcare, although its applicability is not always obvious. Descriptions of Lean Six Sigma in healthcare are often dull and come across as abstract theories and discussions. Sometimes the terminology sounds foreign, if not awkward, to healthcare professionals. This is partly because of Lean Six Sigma's industrial heritage. Thus, it is often difficult for healthcare professionals to see how Lean Six Sigma will work for them. There also seems to be confusion about the application areas for Lean Six Sigma in healthcare. Does it only apply to reducing clinical and medication errors, or does it also apply more generally to improving the administration of healthcare institutions? The answer is that it applies to both of these important areas.

Instead of presenting long explanations and theoretical justifications of what Lean Six Sigma is and how it works, this book provides real examples of healthcare professionals rolling up their sleeves and demonstrating how Lean Six Sigma works in healthcare, while also providing the much requested evidence base showing how effective the projects were in terms of improving quality and reducing costs in healthcare institutions, rather than opinions or "trust me . . . it works" statements. While the specific solutions designed to solve an individual organization's specific quality problems are not generalizable and universally applicable to other institutions, the Lean Six Sigma approach is!

HOW IS THE BOOK ORGANIZED?

Any chapter or case can be read independently. You may read the book in any order you prefer. Each case is self-contained and provides explanations of the concepts, tools, and methods of Lean Six Sigma used to solve the problem. The book is organized as follows. The Introduction presents some of the basic notions of Lean Six Sigma quality management, explains key concepts and terminology, and makes the reading of the cases easier. The introduction is followed by Part I, presenting six articles of a more general nature written by healthcare professionals from a variety of healthcare institutions that engaged in quality improvement, telling how they achieved their results and what they learned. Part II provides seven detailed cases that describe specific applications of Lean Six Sigma to healthcare. Finally, the conclusion provides a discussion of lessons learned and where we go from here.

Acknowledgments

My interest in healthcare quality goes back to 1984 when I assisted Bill Hunter and George Box in teaching a course on quality management at the University of Wisconsin–Madison with participation from the local community, including the City of Madison and Meriter Hospital. Bill's and George's teaching was extremely inspirational and mind-expanding; my intellectual debt to Bill and George is beyond measure. Building on their teaching, I continued to work on combining the fundamental principles of scientific method with the principles of managing for quality. I therefore welcomed the opportunity when in 2001 Professor Ronald Does at the University of Amsterdam invited me to get involved in Six Sigma at the Red Cross Hospital in Beverwijk in the Netherlands. The joint research with Ronald and Jeroen DeMast of the Institute for Business and Industrial Statistics and our collaboration with Dr. Jaap van den Heuvel inspired me to work on this book of case studies. I want to thank them for many inspirational discussions and fruitful collaborations.

My endowed Isenberg Professorship in Integrative Studies at the Isenberg School of Management at University of Massachusetts–Amherst has provided me with the intellectual freedom and resources to pursue research, teaching, and publication in areas such as healthcare quality that fall between traditional academic areas. I especially want to express my sincere gratitude to Gene and Ronnie Isenberg for their unwavering support and friendship. Their clear vision about the importance of integration in a fragmented world of increasing specialization was clearly ahead of its time.

Many people have helped in putting this book together. I want to thank Karen Utgoff for her editorial assistance and uncommon common sense. Her sound advice has had fundamental impact on the content and layout of the text in this book. I also want to thank Bill Tony for his support in the early phases of this project, and Paul O'Mara, Matt Meinholz, and Randy Benson for their steadfast professional help and support throughout this project. I also want to thank Paul and Leayn Tabili for their excellent editorial and typesetting work.

Lastly I want to express my thanks to my wonderful wife Sue Ellen. From the beginning to the end of this book project she has patiently listened to me and provided advice especially on the human and psychological issues related to quality and change management. I want to dedicate this book to our loving friendship!

Introduction:
The Need for Quality
Improvement in Healthcare

Healthcare is heading for a serious crisis worldwide. Reforming and improving healthcare is one of the most troublesome issues facing the United States, Europe, and, indeed, the rest of the world. To illustrate the gravity of the situation, before his recent retirement, the U.S. Comptroller General David M. Walker emphatically stated, "unless we fix our healthcare system—in both the public and private sectors—rising healthcare costs will have severe, adverse consequences for the federal budget as well as the U.S. economy in the future." His dire predictions were backed by budget projections showing that spending on Medicare and Medicaid is expected to increase from 2007 to 2032 by more that 220 percent in constant dollars while the gross domestic product (GDP) is expected to increase by only 71 percent during the same period of time. Similar projections can be made for Europe and other parts of the world.

Some of these cost increases can be attributed to the use of more advanced healthcare procedures, drugs, methods, and treatments. Today we can do much more than we could 50 years ago! Although these advances have contributed to increased longevity and improved quality of life, they also cost money. While some cost increases are unavoidable, a significant part of the cost increases can be attributed to inefficient management of healthcare organizations. Healthcare organizations are rife with quality problems, waste, and inefficiencies. Fortunately, in general, the end result as experienced by patients is of very high quality. However, all too frequently this high level of quality is achieved at unnecessarily high cost via excessive rework and with exceptional efforts to "make the system work."

HEALTHCARE SCIENCE VERSUS
HEALTHCARE MANAGEMENT

To state this calamity differently, the issue is not the science of healthcare. The medical profession has achieved spectacular results, many of which would have been unimaginable just a few years ago! The issue is with the management of healthcare. Unless we get better at managing healthcare, the benefits of the significant advances in the science of healthcare will be offset by inefficiencies in managing our healthcare systems (see Figure I.1). The marvels of modern healthcare science may soon only be affordable by a minority of the population and may need to be rationed in some form or another.

Obviously, the problems are complex. There is no simple solution! To slow down the escalating costs of healthcare while improving quality will require a wide variety of concerted efforts and thoughtful initiatives with input from the political, economic, scientific, and managerial realms as well as healthcare providers and patients. For a broad-based discussion of healthcare problems and possible strategic solutions, see, for example, Porter and Teisberg (2006).

A critical question confronting us is: short of being an omnipotent decision maker, all-powerful politician, or government entity, is there anything we as individuals can do to improve this situation? The answer is yes. Regardless of what eventually will be decided at a political level, any strategic solution must at a minimum satisfy each patient's legitimate expectation of high quality and comply with the equally legitimate and compassionate desires of healthcare professionals to deliver high-quality care. *Quality management will therefore inescapably be an essential part of the solution.* Thus, we can confidently start such initiatives right now! Healthcare professionals can immediately assume leadership and start to deploy quality management principles within individual healthcare institutions to improve the quality of care processes for the benefit of individual patients, healthcare providers, and their institutions. To start a quality improvement initiative requires little in terms of startup costs, can be done within individual institutions, and will pay back the initial investment very quickly. In fact,

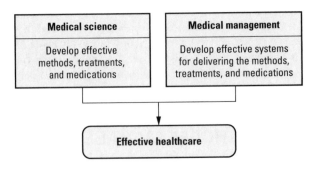

Figure I.1　Effective medical care requires medical science and medical management as equal partners.

experience shows that quality improvement is one of the best return-on-investment initiatives an organization can engage in.

ADAPTING QUALITY MANAGEMENT PRINCIPLES TO HEALTHCARE

When we advocate the use of principles of quality management in healthcare, we must be careful about what we mean. There are many different approaches to quality management. Not all have been equally successful. The more effective approaches have evolved over the past 50 to 60 years and have benefited from exposure to reality—learned from and adapted to what worked and what did not. Some versions of quality management focus on compliance, standards, and voluminous documentation. Compliance with standards is a noble goal. It is clearly part of a mature quality management system. However, by themselves—in isolation, not preceded by aggressive quality improvement efforts—standards and standardization do not necessarily lead to improved results. More often, in fact, such approaches result in bureaucratic, activity-oriented systems that are ineffective and sometimes costly. Unfortunately, in some cases the focus appears to be an obsession with compliance with standards and external mandates, with only scant attention to the needs and expectations of the customers, or in the healthcare context, the patients. Worst of all—sometimes out of fear—satisfying auditors seems to become more important than delivering quality to patients!

LEAN SIX SIGMA: A RESULTS-ORIENTED PROGRAM

Lean Six Sigma (LSS), the general approach to quality management we advocate—and illustrate with a number of case studies in this book—is focused on achieving concrete results, better quality, more efficient processes, and improved value. Results-oriented methodologies, in particular Lean Six Sigma, have demonstrated measurable results in terms of quality, cost, and relevant efficiency metrics on the clinical, operational, and administrative sides of healthcare.

Lean Six Sigma is an effective approach to quality improvement that originated in the manufacturing sector and later was adopted by service industries. A core principle is the elimination of chronic quality problems and waste from processes. Of course, healthcare is very different from manufacturing. However, with appropriate modifications many of the general principles for the elimination and prevention of waste, defects, and quality problems, that have been developed in manufacturing over the years also apply to healthcare. If done sensibly and sensitively, with due consideration of the special circumstances surrounding healthcare and the delicate human elements involved, the application of quality improvement principles will benefit patients and healthcare providers alike while helping to control escalating healthcare costs.

This approach to quality simultaneously benefits patients, healthcare providers, and bottom lines. It is for this reason that we have collected in this book a number of published case studies that directly show, not by high-flying theory, but by concrete examples, how a number of pioneering institutions took it upon themselves to show leadership by implementing Lean Six Sigma in their institutions, large and small, urban and rural. Hopefully, these cases will help demystify Lean Six Sigma, illustrate the application of Lean Six Sigma in a variety of areas, and inspire and encourage healthcare professionals and administrators to try similar approaches in their institutions.

LEAN SIX SIGMA: WHAT IS IT?

As background to the cases in Parts I and II, we briefly summarize the key principles of Lean Six Sigma; for a more detailed discussion, refer to Snee and Hoerl (2003). When considering Lean Six Sigma, it is important to keep in mind that it is not a monolithic, unchanging framework. The general concept constantly evolves; there are many minor variants to the approach, allowing it to be tailored to different circumstances. We provide a relatively generic, mainstream overview as an introduction.

Motorola launched Six Sigma in 1987 as an internal concept for promoting companywide quality improvement. Essentially it was a collection of best practices and proven methodologies for quality improvement developed over many decades prior to that time. It benefited from the wise teaching of Walter A. Shewhart, W. Edwards Deming, Joseph M. Juran, Kaoru Ishikawa, George E. P. Box, and many others. Later, Six Sigma was adopted by and further developed by AlliedSignal (now Honeywell) and General Electric. It gained credibility in the late nineties especially with the strong support of Jack Welch, then CEO of General Electric; see, for example, Snee and Hoerl (2004).

Today Six Sigma is applied worldwide in manufacturing as well as service organizations. Recently, the principles of *lean manufacturing,* essentially a systematic approach to waste reduction originated in the Toyota organization, have been added to the set of tools and approaches, and the name for the combined approach of Six Sigma and lean has morphed into Lean Six Sigma.

Although Six Sigma and lean may have originated in manufacturing, the fundamental principles of LSS are universally applicable to any process, including services, in the private or public sector. Lately LSS has also been applied with success in healthcare as exemplified by the cases in this book. The LSS method is characterized by its process orientation and customer-driven approach as well as its emphasis on deliberate, data-based decision making based on careful analysis, focus on reducing costs, and prudent husbandry of scarce resources. Resources wasted are resources—time and money—that will not benefit patients!

THE DMAIC PROBLEM-SOLVING SEQUENCE

A key feature of the LSS approach to quality improvement that makes it particularly well suited for healthcare is that it is fundamentally similar in spirit and philosophy to good old established medical practice used since the time of Hippocrates:

1. First, carefully define the problem.

2. Then gather all relevant data and information.

3. Proceed to carefully and deliberately diagnose the problem.

4. After completing a thorough diagnosis, with possible additional iterations of more information-gathering and analysis, proceed to propose a remedy.

5. Implement (deploy) the remedy.

6. Finally, check to see if the remedy turned out to be effective.

As in any investigation, it may be necessary to iterate some of these steps. In LSS terminology, the problem-solving strategy deploys five phases—*define* (D), *measure* (M), *analyze* (A), *improve* (I), and *control* (C)—that are rigorously followed whenever a problem, large or small, is approached. The terminology may be different, but the idea is the same. Figure I.2 provides a summary flowchart of the tasks typically performed in each of the five phases of a Lean Six Sigma project.

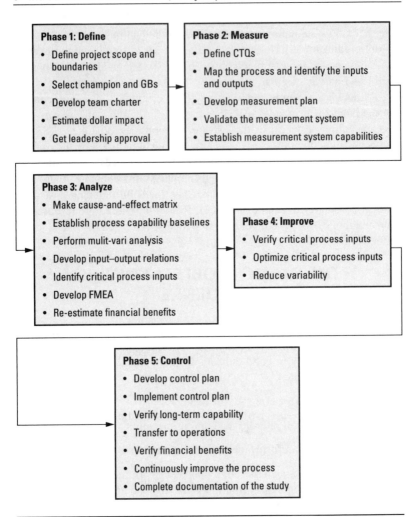

Figure I.2   Summary flowchart of the steps of the define, measure, analyze, improve, and control cycle used in Lean Six Sigma.

Define

In the *define* phase, a problem is selected and a cost–benefit analysis is performed to determine if the project is worthwhile and aligned with strategic goals. If the perceived benefit-to-costs ratio exceeds a certain minimum threshold and the project's goals are clearly aligned with strategic organizational goals, the problem is then scheduled for solution and assigned to a team headed by a Champion from upper management and an employee trained in the Six Sigma methodology, called a Green Belt (GB) or Black Belt (BB); these terms and the organizational structure will be explained in more detail below.

Measure

In the subsequent *measure* phase, baseline data are assembled and the diagnostic process is started in earnest. The problem is then translated into quantifiable terms or concrete, results-oriented metrics via what is called *critical-to-quality* (CTQ) characteristics. For example, training 20 Black Belts in the last fiscal year is not a results-oriented metric, or CTQ. That is an activity-based number typically of little relevance to measurable quality improvement and patient value. Reducing medication errors in a particular department by 50 percent over a period of three months while reducing costs by more than a million dollars on an annual basis, as reported in one of our case studies (see "Lean Six Sigma Reduces Medication Errors"), is an example of concrete, results-oriented, and meaningful metrics. The measure phase typically includes an investigation into the reliability of the measurement process and the quality of the data. The philosophy is that if you can not trust the data, it is hopeless to proceed.

Analyze

The *analyze* phase continues the careful and deliberate diagnosis of the problem and involves an identification of possible causal relationships between inputs and relevant CTQs. The general spirit among the team members should be akin to *detectives setting out to solve a mystery*. Green Belts, Black Belts, and the team members should think of themselves as investigators trying to find the root cause for chronic quality problems and developing solutions that permanently solve the problems. In the analyze phase, the team seeks to determine baseline capabilities of the process based on recent history or for a brief initial period, again using relevant results-oriented metrics. The objective is to assess where we stand before any interventions are made. The baseline capability data often provide new clues that strengthen and refine the diagnosis.

Improve

Once the diagnosis is completed, the team proceeds to the *improve* phase to develop possible solutions to the problem. After deliberations about what constitutes the best solution, the team experiments with new designs, implements process changes, or makes adjustments that are expected to improve the performance of the CTQs. After verification—should the proposed remedy not facilitate the expected improvement—the team needs to try an alternate solution or redo the diagnosis and start again; iterative learning is another way to explain the improvement process.

Control

In the *control* phase, control systems are developed to ensure that improvements are maintained into the future. These are typically based on plots of relevant metrics on control charts. Finally, the new, improved process is handed over to day-to-day operations while the team celebrates its success, disbands, and turns its attention to new problems.

To simplify and guide the LSS effort, each of the five phases of DMAIC involves detailed step-by-step road maps. In addition to strict adherence to the DMAIC problem-solving methodology, the teams are required to make progress reports after each phase of the DMAIC cycle to a representative from upper management called a Champion. Based on the progress reports, the Champion makes a go/no-go decision for the subsequent phase of the project.

ORGANIZATIONAL PRINCIPLES

Lean Six Sigma is more than a set of tools. A crucial aspect for the success of LSS is getting the organizational structure set up appropriately. A fundamental principle underlying LSS is that the deployment is led by the organization's own employees, not by external "expert" consultants that rush in to "solve" their problems. *It is a self-sustaining program that enables an organization to continuously engage in process improvement and organizational innovations using its own brains, knowledge, and ingenuity.*

Quality problems can be classified as either sporadic or chronic. Sporadic problems often receive a lot of management attention and require heroics. Chronic problems, on the other hand are "part of the system," never urgent, "already part of the overhead costs," and no one pays attention to them. However, they are often significant both in terms of patient impact and their costs. No one "owns" chronic problems, and there are no routine management systems for dealing with them. Chronic quality problems can only be solved project by project. These projects are led by small teams that are provided with tools, guidance, resources, and authority from upper management to carry them out.

Lean Six Sigma is based on the philosophy that project teams bring to the problem-solving process extensive knowledge, explicit or tacit, that is essential input for successful solutions and for improving processes— knowledge external consultants rarely have. For example, frontline healthcare providers, with some LSS training, often are in the best position to diagnose quality problems and develop and implement effective solutions and make sure they work. Nothing ever remains the same. When directly engaged with a process after a quality improvement project officially is completed, those intimately involved with the process can continue to learn, adapt to change, and further fine-tune and improve a process.

It would be naive to think that an organization can initiate an effective and successful improvement effort without external help, specifically for training in the early stages, technical assistance, and developing an organizational superstructure. To create the initial capacity to carry out quality improvement projects, selected employees of the organization are typically provided with various levels of training in the LSS methodology. In general, a number of employees receive two weeks of training spread out over several months where they are required to successfully complete a Lean Six Sigma project, after which they receive the title of Green Belt (GB). Others, typically a smaller group, receive four weeks of more in-depth technical training, work on and complete one or two larger projects and, if successful, receive the title of Black Belt (BB). Once the employees have received the title of Green Belt or Black Belt, they continue to lead quality improvement teams and become a real force for innovation and organizational change.

To support the GBs and the BBs in technical, statistical, and managerial matters, a Master Black Belt (MBB) is also usually employed. Often, in the early phases of introducing LSS in an organization, the MBB is an external consultant or someone hired from another organization, with significant training and experience in LSS. In later phases MBBs are recruited from among the best and most successful internal BBs.

LSS LEADERSHIP

As indicated above, the Black Belts and Green Belts manage individual project teams while Master Black Belts coach and assist teams on technical and managerial matters related to carrying out the projects either as needed or on a regularly scheduled basis. Champions are representatives from upper management that play the roles of project owners and project supervisors; see Figure I.3 for a graphical depiction of how a typical LSS program is organized. Champions, as a group, manage the projects collectively, and as individuals manage a few project teams. Collectively, and in close collaboration with the organization's executive leadership to assure strategic alignment, the Champions prioritize and select which projects should be scheduled for solutions. Ultimately, they are responsible for the projects' successful and timely completion.

Individually, the Champions guide the teams, help them fine-tune the project objectives, review the cost–benefit analysis, and, as the project progresses, make sure the teams make progress, stay on schedule, conduct regular and rigorous progress reviews (typically after each of the DMAIC phases), provide necessary resources, help resolve potential conflicts, act as liaison to upper management, and make sure the teams eventually achieve the promised results on time, typically within no more than three to six months.

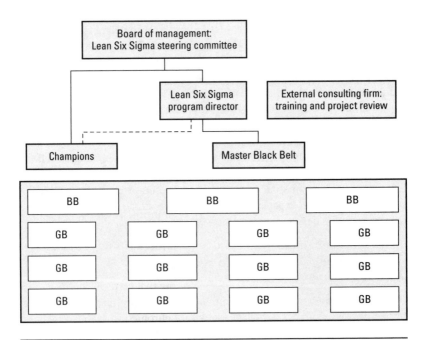

Figure I.3 A typical organizational structure for deploying Lean Six Sigma within a healthcare organization.

LSS DEPLOYMENT STRATEGY

Lean Six Sigma's deployment strategy is based on a coordinated effort of several teams carrying out strategically important, results-oriented improvement projects. Project selection is based on careful translation of the organization's strategy into operational goals. Also note that quality improvement is defined broadly, not just in terms of defects, but in terms of providing better value.

A deployment plan for strategically relevant projects ensures an alignment of project goals with the long-term organizational mission, values, and objectives. Project proposals can be submitted from all levels of the organization, including direct healthcare providers, nurses, doctors, technicians, administrators, and executives. All project proposals are subjected to a rigorous procedure and set of tests to prove their cost–benefit potential, feasibility, scope, and strategic relevance before they are approved and are scheduled for solution. This is a crucial step intended to prevent what in pre–Six Sigma times was called "project mania" where many irrelevant projects were started, often with no clear objectives and goals, frequently dragging on forever without success or significance, and providing little, if any, useful benefit to the organization. It is especially important that the first projects an organization engages in become successful. The first projects must therefore be strategically important, appropriately scoped— not too big and also not too small—and have a high probability of success within a three- to six-month time schedule.

SUMMARY OF CORE PRINCIPLES OF LEAN SIX SIGMA

To sum up, LSS is based on the following core elements:

1. *A structured approach.* A management infrastructure based on Lean Six Sigma's organizational mechanisms, consisting of a task force deployment strategy using Black Belts, Green Belts, and Champions.

2. *Project-based deployment.* Recognizing that chronic quality problems can only be solved on a project-by-project basis, projects based on carefully selected important chronic problems are scheduled for solution and assigned to GB or BB teams. Projects may be classified as either "quick wins" (lean) or "advanced" (Six Sigma). Lean projects apply best practices and typically

involve reduction of lead time, waste, and processing time. Six Sigma projects apply to more general problems and require the use of data-based analytic methods and statistics, including quality improvement and control methods. In all cases the step-by-step problem-solving algorithm of DMAIC is (rigorously) applied. All projects are carefully monitored and held to a time schedule until completed.

3. *Organizational development.* A dedicated group of the organization's employees are trained as Champions, GBs, and BBs and master the tools and techniques of LSS as well as the general concepts of scientific, data-based problem solving.

4. *Organizational anchoring of solutions.* Clearly defined jobs, tasks and responsibilities, standardized procedures, and explicit process controls are part of every improvement project. These structures secure the implementation of solutions and guard against backsliding.

5. *Linking strategy with project selection and evaluation.* Projects scheduled for solution must always be strategically important to the organization. To assure alignment with overall strategic objectives, project performance indicators and results-oriented metrics are developed that, in turn, serve as a basis for project evaluation and selection.

CAUTION: HEALTHCARE INVOLVES DELICATE HUMAN RELATIONS

Before we turn to the short descriptions of each of the cases presented in Parts I and II of this book, we want to provide a few cautionary remarks. Most people immediately associate quality with inspection, checking for defects, uniformity, and, in an extension of this line of thinking, looking for scapegoats to blame when something has gone wrong. That is *not* what LSS is about. Lean Six Sigma is about quality improvement, not quality inspection. Lean Six Sigma does not rely on quality control. Quality is not about scapegoating and assigning blame! Quality improvement is a careful scientific approach to discovering systemic problems and removing root causes of poor quality. It is about preventing quality problems.

It is useful to distinguish between sporadic and chronic quality problems. Although sporadic problems can be very serious and often require managers or employees to perform heroic acts, LSS is primarily about removing chronic, persistent, and systemic quality problems. Unfortunately, heroic actions may occasionally be necessary when something has gone badly wrong, but this is not the primary focus of LSS. However, when we attack chronic quality problems, we typically, as a by-product, also prevent sporadic quality flare-ups from occurring. Lean Six Sigma is about improving systems and the prevention of problems. In that respect it is similar to the concept of preventive medicine.

As mentioned above, quality improvement is not about finding scapegoats and assigning blame. Several of the case studies presented in this book deal with human errors. In some cases, Pareto analysis is used to identify individuals who make more errors than what is typical. It should be noted that in each instance the teams carefully disguised the individuals' names with an identification number. Rather than blaming error-prone staff, in each of the studies the team looked for the deeper causes of the problems, which often resided in the management system. In some of the cases they identified lack of training, lack of standard procedures, or similar systems issues as the root cause for the problems. The authors then proceeded to explain how the LSS team developed better systems, for example better training programs, that, in the end, remedied the problems.

SYSTEMS PROBLEMS

The LSS philosophy is that most people want to do a good job. However, they often lack training, don't know all the details that the job entails, and are let down by the system they work in. Such problems are not within the individual worker's power to solve. There is often little they can do to improve their performance within a dysfunctional system. Rather, to solve such problems is ultimately the responsibility of management as only it has the authority to change and improve the system. It is a well-established rule of thumb among experienced quality professionals that more than 80 percent of all quality problems are systems problems and the responsibility of management to resolve. We stress this point because it is extremely important, especially in the healthcare context. Dealing with defects and errors is a sensitive and delicate matter, especially when it involves human life and health issues. If the issue is not dealt with appropriately, an otherwise well-meaning effort to improve quality can be completely derailed. Or worse, what was intended as an effort to improve healthcare may end up creating an atmosphere of fear.

MINDLESS SEARCH FOR EFFICIENCY

Another danger is a mindless search for efficiency. For example, early industrial attempts to improve efficiency often degenerated into punitive stopwatch studies of frontline workers. If done purely for the understanding of a process and the individual components of a job, time and motion studies may be worthwhile. In fact, such studies can often help simplify a job considerably. However, when misapplied, efficiency studies often turn into an adversarial process between management and those studied. It is human nature to resist such studies. In healthcare the processes involve not only healthcare workers but also patients, all of whom are human beings that deserve to be treated with respect. In interacting with patients it is necessary to treat them individually and provide individualized help and care; they are not nuts and bolts! This implies that there should not be a "standard time" for a task, for example, a diagnosis. Most detrimentally, if efficiency studies end up prescribing fixed time intervals for doctor's office visits or consultation with a nurse, the rigid use of "productivity standards" will most likely harm quality and demoralize healthcare professionals. Indeed, this has been the experience under managed care.

The case studies in this collection all describe projects where results have been achieved by being smarter in how jobs are designed and performed rather than by adding pressure on the people performing the job, or their patients. In each case, the LSS teams reported that efficiency was improved for both patients and employees: costs were reduced, quality was improved, and satisfaction scores were raised. This is a difficult thing to achieve. However, as the cases show, it is possible and it is essential for the success of Lean Six Sigma in healthcare.

OVERVIEW OF THE CASES

The cases and articles that constitute the main bulk of this book are divided into two groups. Part I contains general articles about the implementation of quality improvement in healthcare, and Part II provides a selection of more specific and detailed Lean Six Sigma cases. As a guide to the reader here is a quick summary of each of the articles.

Part I: General Articles on Lean Six Sigma in Healthcare

1. The first article in Part I, written by Dr. Richard Stahl of Yale–New Haven Hospital and General Electric consultants Bradley Schultz

and Carolyn Pexton, is entitled "Healthcare's Horizon: From Incremental Improvement to Designing the Future." The authors first provide an overview of key concepts of Six Sigma. They explain the DMAIC problem-solving cycle as applied to existing processes using examples from the radiology department and the emergency department. They then proceed to explain that especially in healthcare it is often necessary to redesign processes using the *design for Six Sigma* (DFSS) approach. They outline the DFSS process of translating customer expectations into process specifications and design requirements, and introduce the define, measure, analyze, design, and validate (DMADV) problem-solving cycle. The concept of quality function deployment (QFD) and the Kano model for translating customer needs into process specifications are also introduced and briefly explained. The article concludes with a plea for the healthcare industry to gravitate toward evidence-based design of new processes, systems, and structures.

2. In the second article in Part I, entitled "Dutch Hospital Implements Six Sigma," Dr. Jaap van den Heuvel, an MD and the CEO of the Red Cross Hospital in the Netherlands, and his two coauthors describe how the Red Cross Hospital, based on its prior ISO 9000 certification, applied Six Sigma's project management system to achieve a higher success rate and more discipline for its quality improvement projects. As they report, "[Six Sigma's] well-defined and well-turned managerial instruments enhanced the results of improvement projects and, ultimately, maximized the performance of the entire organization." The article also describes a number of specific Six Sigma projects ranging from the clinical to the administrative sides of the hospital, each showing significant improvements in quality while reducing costs.

3. One of the most difficult aspects of successfully implementing Six Sigma is project management. The third article, entitled "A Quest for Quality," written by Rosanne Zimmerman and her coworkers from Hamilton Health Sciences in Canada, describes the importance of employing facilitators to optimize the success rate of quality improvement projects. Although the article does not directly mention Six Sigma, the experiences and lessons learned about project management and facilitation are universal and helpful. Specifically, the authors describe how the facilitators planned group meetings, led teams though the application of quality improvement tools, developed team building skills, and so on. The article briefly describes three successful quality improvement projects in the emergency department.

4. Six Sigma applies universally and is also applicable in smaller institutions and rural hospitals. In the fourth article in Part I, entitled "Taking

Performance to a Higher Level," Greg Stock from the Thibodaux Regional Medical Center, a small, rural not-for-profit hospital in Southern Louisiana, describes how Six Sigma helped achieve impressive results in patient satisfaction, cost savings, and quality improvement. Those improvements, in turn, induced a cultural transformation of the organization. Besides demonstrating several successful projects that saved this small hospital an impressive $450,000 per year while improving quality, the article also describes how Six Sigma "enabled providers to build acceptance and accountability, develop unique problem-solving skills, and link efforts to well-defined organizational objectives."

5. To be successful, healthcare applications of Six Sigma must involve all groups and hierarchal layers of a healthcare organization. However, the involvement of physicians is crucial. As Chip Caldwell, a Six Sigma consultant, Jim Bexler, the CEO of Erlanger Health Systems in Chattanooga, Tennessee, and Tom Gillem, vice president of m21partners in Nashville, argue in their article entitled "Engaging Physicians in Lean Six Sigma," participation and support from physicians in healthcare improvement efforts is critical for success. They explain how "heroic process innovation simply can not be realized without physician engagement." The authors first list eight reasons why physicians may not be interested in Six Sigma. They then proceed to provide guidelines for how to engage physicians, including advice to: a) fully understand physicians' needs, b) build trust between hospital administrators and physicians, c) educate the physicians, and d) engage in win–win projects that will delight the physicians and help them in their work while improving quality and organizational efficiency.

6. The last article in Part I is entitled "Learning from Mistakes." This is a very fine and honest article about what not to do. The article is written by Diana Shaw and her colleagues at Strong Memorial Hospital in Rochester, New York. Although this classic article was published more than 10 years ago and preceded the Lean Six Sigma epoch, the lessons learned by this team are universal and still important for those engaging in quality improvement to internalize. We don't need to make all the mistakes ourselves! We can learn from others. This article should be read by anyone before engaging in Lean Six Sigma, and probably be reread occasionally while involved in managing Six Sigma efforts. This article highlights many of the flaws with the total quality management (TQM) approach that have been remedied with the project management systems of Lean Six Sigma. It is especially informative for anyone having misgivings about Six Sigma or questioning the steps of the DMAIC problem-solving process, the Six Sigma training philosophy, or the Six Sigma project management system.

Should you have such concerns, this article will answer many of your questions about why Six Sigma is organized as it is.

Part II: Cases and Examples of the Use of Lean Six Sigma in Healthcare

In Part II we present concrete cases of applications of Lean Six Sigma in healthcare from a number of healthcare institutions.

1. The first article is written by Yani Benitez, a Six Sigma consultant with BJC HealthCare in St. Louis, and three nurses from Alton Memorial Hospital in Alton, Illinois, part of BJC HealthCare. The case is entitled "Hospital Reduces Medication Errors Using DMAIC and QFD" and describes how Six Sigma was used to reduce work and drastically reduce medication errors. The Six Sigma team applied the DMAIC problem-solving cycle to improve the collaboration between doctors, nurses, and the pharmacy, eliminated redundancy, and standardized the medication order process using a variety of quality improvement tools including quality function deployment (QFD) and control charts.

2. The second case, entitled "Faster Turnaround Time," written by Angelo Pellicone and Maude Martocci, is based on a Six Sigma project conducted at North Shore University Hospital in Manhasset, New York, a part of North Shore–Long Island Jewish Health System in Great Neck, New York. Based on a capstone study, the hospital found that one of their major problems was delays in bed turnaround time resulting in low operating room throughput and emergency department holds that caused adverse effects throughout the hospital. A Six Sigma team was formed to initially focus on one surgical nursing unit. The team followed the DMAIC cycle, made process maps and cause-and-effect diagrams, and established baseline process capabilities. In the analysis phase, the team discovered many clues to the delay in turnaround time, including poor communication and lack of training in using the computer systems. An interesting observation was that the department responsible for the bed tracking system, unlike the general perception, was not causing the problem. The team moved on to the improvement phase and instituted a number of remedies that eventually resulted in cutting the bed turnaround time in half. Finally, in the control phase, the team instituted a control chart to monitor the bed turnaround time to hold on to the gains and prevent backsliding. This initial project was so successful and well received by the staff that it served as a pilot for the rest of the hospital. Moreover, the patient satisfaction score improved significantly.

3. Medication errors are among the most insidious and persistent quality problems in healthcare; see Aspden et al. (2007). The third case, entitled "Lean Six Sigma Reduces Medication Errors," written by Grace Esimai, a PhD statistician, describes how she helped a midsize hospital (which had chosen to remain anonymous) use Lean Six Sigma to drastically reduce errors and cut costs while improving patient satisfaction and employee moral. The case walks the reader step-by-step through each of the phases of the DMAIC process. Based on operational definitions of the various types of errors, the team proceeded to make Pareto charts of the types of errors based on two months of baseline data. From that, a number of root causes, including misunderstanding of guidelines and instructions, were discovered. Interestingly, it was also found that poor communication between nurses and pharmacists was a major problem. This led to two customer surveys, one of the nurses and one of the pharmacists. The surveys provided important information about how to develop better relations between the two groups and hence better collaboration and error reduction. The analysis phase then led to a number of error-reduction solutions that eventually produced an almost 50 percent reduction in medication errors within a few months. The estimated labor cost reduction was more than a million dollars on an annual basis.

4. The fourth case, "Quality Intervenes at a Hospital," is a detailed discussion of the use of Lean Six Sigma to significantly improve scheduling at the interventional radiology department at Nebraska Medical Center, a midsize nonprofit hospital in Omaha, Nebraska. The author, Jennifer Volland, a nurse with an MBA, describes how her team methodically applied the DMAIC problem-solving strategy to eventually discover a number of problems with the scheduling process, implement a number of changes and remedies to the process, and eventually achieve significant improvements. The team was able to eliminate complaints from referring clinics, improve collaboration and efficiency in scheduling, and improve job satisfaction while increasing patient volume by 21 percent over the previous fiscal year.

5. Clinical laboratories are obvious candidates for Lean Six Sigma projects. The fifth case, entitled "Toward Error-Free Lab Work," is written by Nancy B. Riebling, Susan Condon, and Daniel Gopen of the North Shore–Long Island Jewish Health System in Great Neck, New York. This article chronicles how a Lean Six Sigma team achieved a combination of cost reductions and revenue increases that added an estimated $339,000 to the bottom line of the core laboratory. The Six Sigma team methodically went through the DMAIC phases using a variety of concepts and tools

including operational definitions, process maps, Pareto charts, and bench-marking with other reference laboratories. The team determined a few root causes and instituted a staff training program that effectively drove down the error rate. In a parallel project, a Lean Six Sigma team significantly streamlined and improved the movement of specimens around the laboratory. This project included a designed experiment to determine the effect of bar codes, the distribution of specimens, and the experience level of the staff. The experiment helped convince the staff that the lean workflow increased productivity while the bar coding reduced errors. As the authors say in the conclusion, "lean and change management gave the team the tools it needed to fix the process and sustain the improvements."

6. The sixth case, entitled "Health Care Department Reduces Cycle Time and Errors," is written by Donna Powers and Mary Paul, also from North Shore–Long Island Jewish Health System in New York. A sensitive issue in healthcare is that despite many errors and rework along the way, high quality is eventually often delivered to the patient. Doctors, nurses, and other healthcare professionals do a yeoman's job to provide the best possible care. The problem is with the system they work within, not their professionalism, dedication, and compassion. The high-quality end product is sometimes achieved in spite of a lot of inefficiencies via expensive hero-ics, especially from nurses and nurse assistants. Since the Long Island cam-pus's department of ambulatory chemotherapy and transfusion (ACT) in this case had very high patient satisfaction, there was initially resistance to changing anything. However, after documenting the chronic state of rework and inefficiency in the billing process, estimated to cost between $250,000 to $500,000 in the fiscal year 2004, the clinical staff was convinced that improving quality would allow them more face time with patients. The case then documented how the team was able to identify and remedy key sources of billing errors and reduce the error rate by 72 percent while significantly reducing the billing cycle time. As part of the project, the team also intro-duced a new scheduling system that positively impacted the patients. As a result, the department was able to maintain its high patient satisfaction score while eliminating a random billing check function, saving an esti-mated $202 per patient, or about $4 million per year.

7. The seventh case study, "Standardizing Healthcare Projects," is written by a team of professors and Six Sigma consultants and the CEO of a large hospital in the Netherlands. This team has, over the past several years, been involved with close to 100 Six Sigma projects, and from these they have extracted common patterns and devised a set of generic templates

that can help a novice Six Sigma team get through the define and measure phases of the DMAIC cycle. The six generic templates are illustrated with numerous examples from both the clinical and the administrative sides of hospital operations.

CONCLUSION

It is easy to feel discouraged about the overwhelming healthcare problems we face. It seems like costs are ever rising while quality is deteriorating. We may feel that solving the problems with healthcare is beyond the reach of most healthcare professionals. However, the case studies in this book demonstrate that individual healthcare professionals and administrators can assume leadership and play a decisive role in improving the quality of care. Regardless of what eventually gets worked out at the political level, in the end, at the direct healthcare provision level, quality management and especially quality improvement will inescapably have to be part of the solution. The cases discussed in the following chapters of this book will provide you with a head start in understanding how Lean Six Sigma works in healthcare and how you can get involved and make a difference.

References

Aspden, P., J. A. Walcott, J. L. Bootman, and L. R. Cronenwett, eds. 2007. *Preventing Medication Errors.* Washington, DC: The National Academies Press.

David, M. 2007. "Health Care 20 Years from Now: Taking Steps Today to Meet Tomorrow's Challenges." September, 2007. GAO-07-1155SP. See www.gao. gov/cgi-bin/getrpt?GAO-07-1155SP.

DeKoning, H., J. Verver, J. van den Heuvel, S. Bisgaard, and R. Does. 2006. "Lean Six Sigma in Healthcare," *Journal of Healthcare Quality* 28, no. 2: 4–11.

Juran, J. M. 1989. *Juran on Leadership for Quality.* New York: The Free Press.

Porter, M. E., and E. O. Teisberg. 2006. *Redefining Health Care.* Cambridge, MA: Harvard Business School Press.

Snee, R. D., and R. W. Hoerl. 2003. *Leading Six Sigma.* Upper Saddle River, NJ: FT Prentice Hall.

———. 2004. *Six Sigma Beyond the Factory Floor.* Upper Saddle River, NJ: Pearson Education.

Check www.asq.org/sixsigma/terms/index.html.

Part I

General Articles on Lean Six Sigma in Healthcare

Healthcare's Horizon

From Incremental Improvement to Designing the Future

Richard Stahl, MD, Yale–New Haven Hospital,
Bradley Schultz and Carolyn Pexton, GE Medical Systems

Impressive examples over the past several years illustrate the value of utilizing Six Sigma and related best practices for healthcare quality and process improvement.

Providers, however, continue to face a daunting and escalating array of challenges. Regulatory pressures, increased competition, cost management issues, workforce shortages and rising consumerism all vie for attention and remediation.

Occupying an increasingly prominent place on the healthcare executive's radar screen are issues involving clinical quality and patient safety. Instances of overuse, underuse and misuse of healthcare services have been costly to patients, providers and payers.

Prompted by illuminating reports from the Institute of Medicine[1, 2] and scrutiny from groups such as Leapfrog, providers are seeking effective methods for both optimizing the care they deliver and documenting the improvements.

It is a pivotal moment in the history of medicine—one offering great promise through rapidly advancing technology and tremendous pressure to deliver better care to more people for less cost.

At this juncture, then, it seems an appropriate time for reflection—both on the progress made through Six Sigma applications and the realm of opportunities for the future. Drawing from research and organizational experience, we can evaluate achievements and explore the next phase in reshaping the industry.

APPLICATIONS TO HEALTHCARE

The DMAIC (define, measure, analyze, improve and control) approach works quite well for any service line or process that can furnish measurable response variables.

Reprinted with permission from Richard Stahl, Bradley Schultz, and Carolyn Pexton, "Healthcare's Horizon," *Six Sigma Forum Magazine* 2, no. 2: 17–26.

Generally, four groups of metrics or response variables in healthcare may define a delivery system's performance:

- Service level.

- Service cost.

- Customer satisfaction.

- Clinical excellence.

Service level metrics indicate the ability of the system's performance to meet the expectations of patients, referring physicians and other stakeholders—critical to quality parameters (CTQs).

Each set of metrics has specific parameters. Service level indicators may be generalized as access to care, wait time, service time and information conveyance time. Service cost indicators include cost per unit of service, labor productivity and other factors associated with the cost of providing service. Customer satisfaction indicators may be segmented into specific groups such as patient and family, referring physician, staff and payer.

Clinical excellence indicators may relate to a particular treatment pathway or department, such as compliance with guidelines for prescription of aspirin to myocardial infarction patients or reduction of rates of infection contracted in a hospital or other healthcare facility. Figure 1 illustrates sample metrics from an emergency department.

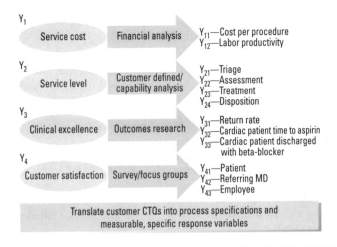

Figure 1 Response variables.

Most healthcare organizations measure performance using some combination from these four groups, but such analysis can be misleading since the metrics often represent an average. Customers rarely experience the average performance of a system—instead, they tend to experience the variability.

FROM MANUFACTURING TO MEDICINE

Six Sigma came slowly to healthcare and initially was met with some skepticism. This hesitancy stemmed in part from disparities between processes driven by humans vs. automated or engineered processes.

In manufacturing, it's quite possible to eliminate most—if not all—human variability through automation, creating precise measurement of assignable causes of variation. In healthcare, however, the delivery of patient care is largely a human process, and the causes of variability are often more subtle and difficult to quantify.

The challenge for healthcare institutions and staff as they begin to embrace Six Sigma is to find a way to leverage the data to drive human behavior. Where the approach seems to have had greatest success, providers combined a strong technical strategy (Six Sigma) with a strong cultural strategy, such as a change acceleration process, and a sound operationalizing mechanism, such as GE Medical Systems' Work-Out, Motorola's Leadership Jump Start, lean, Pareto analysis or decision trees. This is illustrated in Figure 2.

Leveraging all three aspects has led to notable results. Most projects, however, involved optimizing existing processes and retaining systems and

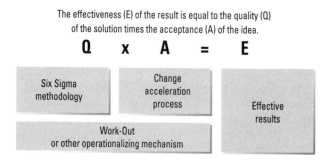

The effectiveness (E) of the result is equal to the quality (Q) of the solution times the acceptance (A) of the idea.

$$Q \quad \times \quad A \quad = \quad E$$

| Six Sigma methodology | Change acceleration process | Effective results |

Work-Out or other operationalizing mechanism

Figure 2 Formula for effective results.

structures bound by capital investment and traditional grouping by function. A hospital's IT system, for example, may not fully support changing a given process, but the facility might decide to simply optimize around it until the investment is retired.

Service delivery methods in healthcare have also become entrenched and often run counter to the notion of customer centricity. It's common in many facilities, for instance, to take the patient to the care rather than bring the care to the patient. Clearly, we need new models to create a system that genuinely meets patient needs.

A BRIEF OVERVIEW OF DMAIC

To implement the right solution to a problem, you need to understand the degree to which different factors may impact the variability of the project's response variable (Y) before specific solutions are designed. Projects tend to focus on response variables from the four groups mentioned earlier.

The initial define and measure phases of a project essentially involve translating the voice of the customer, or CTQs, into measurable response variables. Customer expectations—whether patients, referring physicians, staff or payers—are then used to establish process specifications for those response variables. A measurement of the process capability to meet CTQs is performed, and the end result is expressed as a sigma level or defects per million opportunities (DPMO). This concept is shown in Figure 3, using cycle time for reporting radiology results.

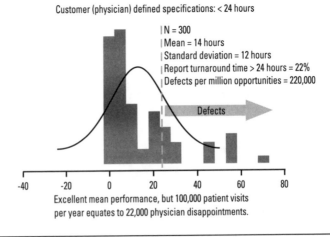

Customer (physician) defined specifications: < 24 hours

N = 300
Mean = 14 hours
Standard deviation = 12 hours
Report turnaround time > 24 hours = 22%
Defects per million opportunities = 220,000

Defects

-40   -20   0   20   40   60   80

Excellent mean performance, but 100,000 patient visits
per year equates to 22,000 physician disappointments.

Figure 3 Capability analysis: report turnaround time.

In the analyze phase, the team identifies the causal factors (X's) likely to have the greatest impact on the response variable (Y). These factors are classified as either controllable or uncontrollable. If a factor (X) is controllable and contributes significantly to variability in the response variable (Y), then an opportunity to achieve a better result presents itself by controlling the causal factor.

On the other hand, if the primary causal factors are uncontrollable, a new process must be built to withstand that variability to the degree possible. Many factors in healthcare are quite predictable, though uncontrollable—such as arrival rate at the emergency room. See "Common Emergency Department Critical to Quality Factors."

In healthcare, the improve and control phases can be most challenging since they often involve changing human behavior. It probably comes as no surprise to healthcare professionals that organizational structure can actually inhibit process thinking. Inherently, there are multiple silos across a typical facility and few examples of big picture oversight to unify conflicting agendas and constituencies.

COMMON EMERGENCY DEPARTMENT CRITICAL TO QUALITY FACTORS

Quality:

- Accuracy of diagnosis.
- Appropriateness of treatment.
- Timeliness of service.
- Wait times.
- Exam and treatment.
- Testing and report turnaround.
- Staff availability.
- Bed availability in emergency department and hospital.
- Responsiveness to squads.

Satisfaction of patient and referring doctor.

Cost of operations.

Productivity and workflow.

The control phase, therefore, may require dismantling root-bound bureaucracies growing around ancient processes. To achieve long-term success, this must be accompanied by new control measures and process metrics to drive behavior changes.

Another challenge for healthcare is to institutionalize the wins—in other words, to translate the results from one area to another. For example:

- Adopt best practices to improve bed turnover time from a given inpatient unit to all hospital units.

- Translate ventilator weaning protocols from one intensive care unit to another.

FROM HERE TO FUTURITY

Mistakes can be costly in any industry, and there are essentially three ways to approach them. Ignore them and hope for the best (not advisable in most cases); find and fix them within existing processes; or prevent them from occurring in the first place by designing processes correctly from the ground up.

Using the DMAIC approach (the find and fix method), many institutions have seen significant improvement in various clinical and operational processes. When coupled with proven change management and decision-making techniques, some have even been able to induce a beneficial transformation in the organizational culture.

But quantum leap changes in the delivery of healthcare (and the prevention of errors through ground floor development) will not come about until providers begin the process of actually designing for Six Sigma. In *Six Sigma: The Breakthrough Management Strategy Revolutionizing the World's Top Corporations,* author Mikel Harry discusses the limits of traditional Six Sigma initiatives:

> The closer companies come to achieving Six Sigma, the more demanding the improvements become. At 4.8 sigma, companies hit a wall that requires a redesigning of processes, known as design for Six Sigma.[3]

This wall is often felt at significantly lower sigma levels in healthcare and consists of bricks retained from old systems and structures. To get through this wall and create quantum leap change, healthcare will have to adopt breakthrough or revolutionary thinking in how systems are designed and built to optimize the interaction of people, processes and technology.

A BRIEF OVERVIEW OF DFSS

The primary difference between DMAIC and design for Six Sigma (DFSS) is that statistical tools are used to design a new service delivery system, process or tool rather than to improve the existing system. Customer expectations are translated into process specifications and then into system design requirements. These, in turn, flow down into subsystem and process design requirements.

Elements such as service, the care delivery model, supporting systems and structures and facilities are aligned with the resulting design specifications. Similar to DMAIC, DFSS is a five-step process represented by the acronym DMADV (define, measure, analyze, design and validate). Figure 4 is a design process map, basically a criteria-rating matrix that

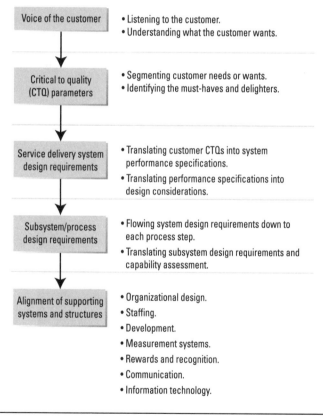

Figure 4   Design process map.

translates iteratively into system design requirements and then into subsystem requirements—drilling down into each level in order to design the process correctly the first time.

ORGANIZATIONAL READINESS FOR DFSS

It is important to note that not all organizations are ready for DFSS. Healthcare institutions can be assessed for readiness along a change continuum, illustrated in Figure 5. Those at the far left have fundamentally unstable operations and service delivery processes. The environment is typically chaotic and repeatability is often dependent on the performance of a few who seem to understand the "magic" involved.

In these institutions, substantial improvement may be achieved through developing and operationalizing procedures that document the magic and begin moving it into the world of science.

This approach is often referred to in DMAIC as a PM/CE/CNX/SOP approach—simply a shorthand method of communicating the following:

- PM = process map.

- CE = cause-effect.

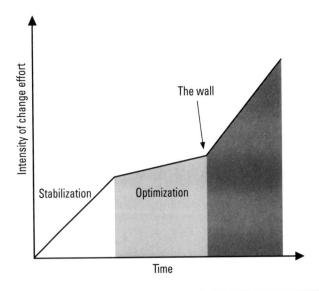

Figure 5 The wall of change efforts.

- CNX = controllable, not controllable, experimental variables.

- SOP = standard operating procedure.

The team first gains a common understanding through process mapping (PM). Brainstorming then follows to discover causes of process variability and assess the effect (CE). Drivers of variability are classified as controllable, not controllable or experimental (CNX).

In the analyze phase of a project, the contribution to variation of the experimental variables is quantified, but the institution may not realize immediate gains by developing SOPs targeted at controllable variables.

In the second stage, processes are stabilized but not yet optimized. The performance service delivery may be stable and repeatable, but still fail to meet customer expectations or operate at lower efficiency and higher cost. In these cases the application of DMAIC will provide the mechanism for process optimization. This occurs by developing a sound understanding of the mathematical relationship between specific response variables (Y's) and their causal factors (X's).

Organizations eventually reach the previously mentioned wall where further optimization of existing systems and structures is no longer feasible. The wall is unavoidable as customer expectations increase and the retention of legacy systems restricts improvement. Design then becomes an important component of the strategy for transformation.

When considering the application of DMAIC or DFSS to a process, the following considerations become relevant:

- To what extent does the current process meet customer expectations?

- Does it require decreased variability alone or a radical shift in mean?

- How committed are you to current legacy systems that support this process?

- What new developments are on the horizon? For example, new pick sheet of materials needed for operating room cases, new service line or center of excellence, renovation of facility or new facility.

An example of a process improvement or solution design continuum is shown in Table 1.

DFSS may be the better approach in cases where the process is simply too broken to satisfy customer expectations or further optimization is constrained by legacy systems and structures. The development of new

Table 1 Process improvement/solution design continuum.

Improvement objectives	Stabilization	Optimization	Transformation
Methods	Work-Out Kaizen Quality circles	Six Sigma—DMAIC Lean thinking Total quality management	Six Sigma—DFSS
When to use	Issues or drivers of variability are well understood. Primary concern is building consensus on solutions.	Causal factors or drivers of variability not well understood. Not in a position to build consensus on solutions.	White paper improvement initiative or development of new and future services designed to exceed customer expectations.
Examples	Stabilization of service level metrics such as wait time through role clarity and standard operating procedures.	• Optimization of operating room capacity utilization. • Optimization of emergency department or radiology throughput.	• New operating room pick sheet. • New service line. • Renovated facility. • New hospital.

opportunities also invites DFSS as a mechanism to design specifically for customer CTQs as opposed to cloning old processes that may fall short.

THE DMADV PROCESS

The define and measure phases of a DMADV project are similar to those of DMAIC in collecting and using voice of the customer data to develop process performance specifications.

The difference with DMADV is that we're often dealing with new products or services, so measuring existing performance against specifications is not possible. With DMADV, the goal is to predict the performance of the new product or service and facilitate evaluation and selection of the best design alternative.

To accomplish this ambitious task of translating voice of the customer data into actionable design criteria, there is a commonly used tool known as quality function deployment (QFD). QFD is an advanced criteria-rating matrix, used in DMADV to:

- Identify customer needs or CTQs (the whats).

- Weight customer needs by order of importance.

- Identify product and service features that meet CTQs (the hows).

- Evaluate the ability of each feature to satisfy each need.

For a new hospital service line, this process would be repeated three times. The first iteration would match customer needs with specific service line features. In successive efforts, the hows become the whats.

The second iteration matches the features against system-level requirements. In the last iteration, system-level requirements are translated into subsystem-level requirements. A QFD for a new emergency and trauma center illustrates the concept in Table 2.

Customer expectations are brainstormed and weighted in the left-hand column. Potential system requirements to satisfy these expectations are brainstormed in the right-hand column.

Table 2 Quality function deployment for new emergency and trauma center—requirements.

Y's		*X*'s
Customer expectations	**Importance**	**System requirements**
No delays to service due to parking	1	Parking and location signage well identified
Ease of entrance identification and location	1	Dedicated emergency room parking within 100 yards of emergency department
Ease of triage identification and location	2	Internal building signage clearly identifies location
		Standardized triage process
Comfort and safety of wait area	3	No triage delays
		Door to doctor time under 30 minutes
		User-friendly concentric wait area

Continued

Table 2 *Continued.*

Y's		*X*'s
Customer expectations	**Importance**	**System requirements**
Minimal wait time to see doctor	4	Metal detectors at entrance
		Staffing by arrival pattern demand
Minimal wait time to receive treatment	4	Patient communication model designed and caregivers trained
		Mechanisms to ensure staff accountability
Privacy	3	
To be kept informed of process status	4	Accurate diagnostics
		Diagnostic cycle time specifications
		Quality therapeutics
Quality care	5	Decision to disposition cycle time less than 15 minutes
Positive caregiver interaction	5	
		Coordination of aftercare by emergency department
Understand aftercare requirements	4	Frequent patient contact and information exchange
		Privacy of triage spaces
		Privacy of treatment spaces
		Availability of treatment supplies at point of care
		Point-of-care testing

Each system-level requirement is evaluated for its ability to satisfy each customer requirement using a high, medium and low scoring system, as in Figure 6. The system requirement score in the bottom row of the table indicates its relative importance. The customer expectation score in the table's right-hand column indicates the extent to which this expectation is covered by the listed systems requirements and can be compared to the weight of the associated customer expectation.

System design requirements can then be sorted in order of importance, as in the Pareto chart in Figure 7. The system design requirements become the expectations (*Y*'s) for the next flowdown, and the process is repeated two more times.

Customer expectation	Importance	Staffing by arrival pattern demand	Accurate diagnostics	Mechanisms to ensure staff accountability	Quality therapeutics	Door to doctor time under 30 minutes	Coordination of aftercare by emergency department	Frequent patient contact and information exchange	No triage delays	Patient communication model designed and caregivers trained	Diagnostic cycle time specifications	Decision to disposition cycle time less than 15 minutes	Standardized triage process	Availability of treatment supplies at point of care	User-friendly concentric wait area	Metal detectors at entrance	Privacy of triage spaces	Privacy of treatment spaces	Internal building signage clearly identifies location	Point-of-care testing	Parking and location signage well identified	Dedicated emergency room parking within 100 yards of emergency department	Total
Positive caregiver interaction	5	H	H	H	H	M	M	H	M	H	L	M	L	M	L	L	L	L		M			390
Quality care	5	H	H	M	H	H	H	M	M	L	H	M	M	M	L	L	L	L		M			400
Minimal wait time to receive treatment	4	H	H	M	M	H	L		H		M	L	M										200
Minimal wait time to see doctor	4	H		M		H			H				M										132
To be kept informed of process status	4	M		H		L	H	H	L	H	L	M	M										192
Understand aftercare requirements	4		H	M	H		H	H			M	M	M										192
Comfort and safety of wait area	3	L		L					L						H	H			M			L	75
Privacy	3			L				L						M			H	H		L			72
Ease of triage identification and location	2																		H				18
Ease of entrance identification and location	1																		H		H	M	21
No delays to service due to parking	1																				H	H	18
Total		177	162	138	138	136	136	135	106	101	78	58	56	39	37	37	37	37	36	33	18	15	

Figure 6   Quality function deployment for new emergency and trauma center—results.
Source: GE Medical Systems.

On the surface, this process may seem arbitrary and subjective. If executed correctly, however, using voice of the customer data to drive the importance of the whats and sound capability data to impact the hows, a very clear picture of overall design requirements and the trade-off between competing interests will emerge with clarity.

It is important to note all customer needs are not created equal in this process. Features that currently exceed customer expectations and are considered delighters will quickly become expected must-haves tomorrow.

This concept is illustrated using Kano's model in Figure 8 and must be considered carefully in assigning importance to customer needs. The model is followed by an illustration of the first iteration of the QFD process that matches features with customer needs.

The define and measure phases of a DMADV project may be summarized as a process of CTQ flowdown. The analyze phase can be summarized

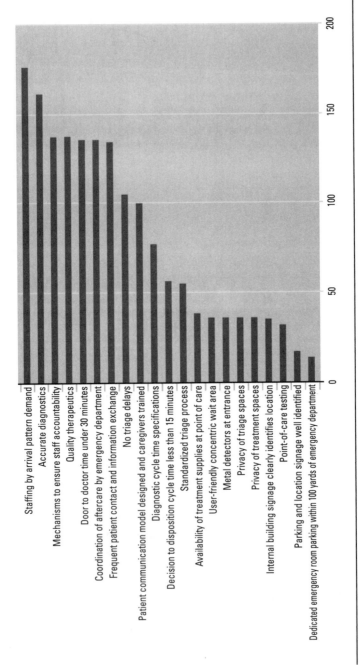

Figure 7   Emergency and trauma center Pareto chart.
Source: GE Medical Systems.

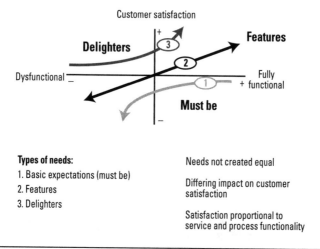

Figure 8 Kano's model.

as a process of capability flow-up. This is where DMAIC and DMADV differ significantly.

In DMAIC, an understanding of causal factors on a specific process outcome is quantified mathematically. In DMADV, a specific process supporting a service line feature and customer need may not exist. Where it does, capability can be measured directly as illustrated in the DMAIC section.

In cases involving new processes, systems and structures, the capability may be projected or forecast using modeling. In healthcare, the models most relevant to a new service line are those targeted at understanding capacity, patient queuing, provider resource allocation and patient routing. This concept is illustrated in Figure 9.

For a healthcare service line, the end result of the analyze phase of a DMADV project is twofold:

1. Develop a mathematical expression of customer needs translated to specific service line features, service delivery system, and service subsystem and process design specification.

2. Match needs and requirements against a mathematical expression of existing or forecast proposed process capabilities.

During the design phase, an optimal design is selected and implemented based on the merging of the CTQ flow-down and the capability flow-up into an integrated design scorecard. Capability forecasting and analysis provides insight into how well design requirements will be met, and the

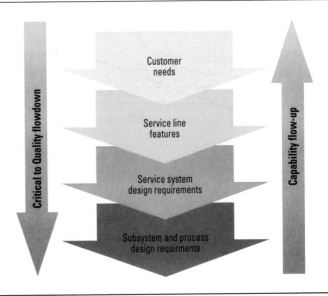

Figure 9 DFSS process.
Source: GE Medical Systems.

QFD translates this into customer satisfaction. The result is a formalized, mathematical model for understanding customer impact associated with specific design alternatives and trade-offs.

Finally, in the validate phase, the actual performance from a subsystem is measured against predicted performance through the confirmation of customer satisfaction. In a manufacturing environment this is achieved through component, subsystem and system-level testing.

In healthcare, however, the opportunity to test segments of the service line may or may not exist. What becomes more important in a healthcare application of DMADV is the degree to which appropriate controls are operationalized to consistently yield predictable results.

Full realization of designed service line entitlements depends on translating the vision of these entitlements to specific behaviors. This requires appropriately targeted changes in recruitment, staff development, measurement systems, performance evaluation, incentives, communication and information technology.

The validation phase of a DMADV project also affords the opportunity to rethink many institutional processes, systems and structures. For example, evaluating design alternatives for a new imaging department may indicate the existing patient registration process will not meet customer expectations. Redesign of this process should trigger rethinking of patient registration across the institution and, at the very least, provide a structured approach to institutional transformation of service.

MEASURABLE DMAIC SUCCESSES

As a methodology for process and quality improvement, Six Sigma has demonstrated its ability to adapt to virtually any process—including patient care. Recorded achievements do not seem to be based on the type or demographics of the organization. Six Sigma has taken root in a wide variety of settings: within individual departments, throughout small, rural hospitals, within large teaching facilities and across multihospital systems.

When appropriately implemented with leadership support and the utilization of change management techniques to address cultural barriers and build acceptance, Six Sigma has achieved measurable success.

The DMAIC approach has been deployed in hospitals and health systems to improve service levels, cost productivity and customer satisfaction. Conceding the inherent distinctions between manufacturing and medicine, however, it's important to acknowledge the impact of human variability on statistical process control and the importance of cultivating acceptance for service-based change initiatives.

WHAT'S NEXT?

Building on the success of the DMAIC model, the next platform for healthcare will likely follow the DFSS approach with continued emphasis on acceptance. DMAIC optimizes existing processes, while DFSS can be used to create and institute an entirely new model for healthcare. Both promises and pitfalls accompany current applications of Six Sigma within healthcare, and organizations will need to carefully assess their own unique needs and preparedness for either targeted or systemic change.

The 21st-century healthcare organization faces multiple challenges. Some are complex, long-standing and unresolved issues, and others are emerging trends:

- Workforce shortages.

- Rising consumerism and patient expectations.

- The Health Insurance Portability and Accountability Act of 1996 and other compliance issues.

- Quality and patient safety.

- Reimbursement issues.

- Aging of the population.

- Regulatory constraints.

- Increasing acuity of illness.

- Disaster preparedness.

Driven by a confluence of such significant factors, the healthcare industry may soon gravitate toward an evidence-based design of new systems and structures as a more verifiable and sustainable way to deliver optimal patient care.

There are no easy answers and no overnight solutions. It will take a considerable commitment and a concerted effort on the part of all stakeholders to embrace a new paradigm and build a better healthcare system by design.

References

1. Institute of Medicine, *Crossing the Quality Chasm: A New Health System for the 21st Century,* National Academy Press, 2001.
2. Institute of Medicine, *To Err Is Human: Building a Safer Health System,* National Academy Press, 1999.
3. Mikel Harry and Richard Schroeder. *Six Sigma: The Breakthrough Management Strategy Revolutionizing the World's Top Corporations,* Currency, 2000.

Bibliography

A New Vision for Healthcare, Committee for Economic Development, 2002.

Burda, David, ed., "By the Numbers," *Modern Healthcare,* Dec. 24, 2001.

Chassin, M.R., "Is Health Care Ready for Six Sigma Quality?" *Milbank Quarterly,* Nov. 4, 1998.

Chowdhury, Subir, *Design for Six Sigma: The Revolutionary Process for Achieving Extraordinary Profits,* Dearborn Trade Publishing, 2002.

Pande, Peter S., Robert P. Neuman and Roland R. Cavanagh. *The Six Sigma Way: How GE, Motorola and Other Top Companies Are Honing Their Performance,* McGraw-Hill, 2000.

Dutch Hospital Implements Six Sigma

Even Small Projects Can Make a Big Difference

Jaap van den Heuvel, Red Cross Hospital, Ronald J.M.M. Does, University of Amsterdam, and Søren Bisgaard, University of Massachusetts Amherst and University of Amsterdam

Red Cross Hospital in Beverwijk, the Netherlands, is a 384-bed, medium-sized general hospital, with a staff of 930 and a budget of $70 million. In addition to being a general healthcare provider, Red Cross Hospital is the base for a 25-bed national burn care center that provides services to all of the Netherlands. In 2002, it admitted 11,632 patients, performed 8,269 outpatient treatments and received 190,218 visits to its outpatient units.

During the past four years, Red Cross Hospital's management and employees invested significant resources in building a quality assurance system, and at the end of 2000, the hospital was awarded an ISO 9002 certification. After that, management began undertaking quality improvement projects on a regular basis, but it was doing so without the benefit of Six Sigma's project management system.

LIFE BEFORE SIX SIGMA

The hospital's initial quality improvement approach appeared to work reasonably well. However, management soon recognized its control of projects was less than effective:

- Project goals were often poorly aligned with the hospital's strategic goals.

- There was no systematic way to determine a project's relevance and contribution to the long-term strategy.

Reprinted with permission from Jaap van den Heuvel, Ronald J. M. M. Does, and Søren Bisgaard, "Dutch Hospital Implements Six Sigma," *Six Sigma Forum Magazine* 4, no. 2: 11–14.

- There was no standardized procedure for evaluating a project's cost-effectiveness.

- Management had difficulty making project go/no-go decisions. Projects were generally initiated because management thought they would make a contribution to quality of care.

- Management was not able to access the potential savings of alternative projects.

- Once a project was started, management did not have reliable information about its status until it was finished. Each project had different milestones, and progress could not be evaluated and compared to other projects.

Management was basically navigating in the dark.

The management team and employees were frustrated because the hospital lacked a standardized project management approach. Time was frequently wasted—when each new project was started, the approach, project documentation and planning had to be developed from scratch. For that and other reasons, management had problems properly training its employees in project management. Though the hospital had organized training, the results were meager and disappointing.

Another problem was management expected employees to work on projects in addition to performing their usual duties. This might appear to be an inexpensive approach, but it seriously delayed potential savings. Ironically, management was mostly unaware of this unfortunate situation because of its poor management controls. Had management been in a position to determine the results of a project in advance, it would have been able to make more appropriate decisions about employee time allocations to projects. Fortunately, management learned employees should be relieved of some of their usual duties when working on a project.

WHY SIX SIGMA?

Six Sigma incorporated a number of quality management techniques that helped resolve some of the problems at Red Cross Hospital. Management believed its implementation of Six Sigma was successful for several reasons:

- *Philosophy:* Because Six Sigma is based on scientific principles, decisions were based on facts and data instead of feelings and intuition. Projects were not initiated when estimated savings were below management-defined thresholds.

- *Project management:* Projects were managed strictly according to the five phases of the define, measure, analyze, improve, control (DMAIC) methodology. Each phase was completed only after specific milestones were reached.[1] At any given time, it was possible to determine a specific project's progress in a unified way within departments and across the entire organization.

- *Well-defined roles and responsibilities:* Six Sigma assigned specific roles—Yellow Belt, Green Belt (GB), Black Belt (BB), Champion and Master Black Belt (MBB)—to those involved. Explicitly defined roles and expected contributions were important during the organizational change effort and contributed to the success of a project.

- *Tools and techniques:* Six Sigma employed a variety of tools and statistical techniques. Software tools were used to make the techniques available and accessible to people with little or no training.

- *Well-defined interfaces with the existing organization:* Six Sigma provided a detailed blueprint that linked it to the existing organization. Specifically, Six Sigma's tight project organization operated across all hierarchical layers of the hospital. All relevant information and responsibilities could be brought together while the business continued to operate.

Six Sigma was not just an idea or another trick to organize improvement projects. Its set of well-defined and well-tuned managerial instruments enhanced the results of improvement projects and, ultimately, maximized the performance of the entire organization.

To implement Six Sigma at Red Cross Hospital, management had to customize and adapt some of the standard Six Sigma management concepts so they better applied to the healthcare industry. For example, adjustments had to be made because Red Cross Hospital was much smaller than the typical organizations that implement Six Sigma.

Management also had to address concerns regarding the culture of its nonprofit, service organization and the differences between it and an industrial for-profit company's explicit focus on financial results. Fortunately, it was relatively easy to convince the skeptics by explaining that more money for the hospital means happier and healthier patients. In this respect, Red

Cross Hospital's experience parallels the implementation of Six Sigma at Thibodaux Regional Medical Center in Louisiana.[2]

THE IMPLEMENTATION

Six Sigma was initiated at Red Cross Hospital by an external consulting company during a one-day training session for upper management at the end of 2001. The management team consisted of two directors and the managers of the hospital's four divisions. The quality manager was introduced to Six Sigma in January 2002, and she enthusiastically went through intensive BB training that spring.

After the quality manager completed her BB course, 16 employees enrolled in in-house GB training provided by the consulting company in September 2002. Though all GB trainees were required to participate in one Six Sigma project, one hospital director also participated in the first wave of GB projects.

During the course of two separate three-day periods, every participant was required to produce documented results. No GB project was allowed to proceed to the subsequent phase until the preceding phase was completed. Participants had to present their results twice in front of the entire group, the second time being a presentation of their final results.

Because of the hospital's small size, teams were made up exclusively of GBs, each typically spending two days a week on the project. Considering the hospital's budget and savings potential, management used $25,000 estimated savings as its financial threshold for initiating a project. After completing the first wave, management immediately started a second group of 15 GBs in February 2003, a third group of 13 GBs in September 2003, a fourth group of 14 GBs in February 2004 and a fifth group of 17 GBs in September 2004.

The Six Sigma approach was well received by employees. The teams believed it supported them throughout the entire process of a project. The data-driven approach was helpful in establishing support during the implementation of the results. The data proved convincing and, in many cases, minimized emotional resistance.

Initially, the hospital's BB performed the role of MBB on a part-time basis. This quickly proved inadequate as the number of GBs increased. Since management wanted to deploy Six Sigma relatively quickly, it decided to hire a full time MBB from outside the hospital. Fortunately, it was able to hire a BB with previous experience from DAF, a Dutch truck manufacturer now owned by Paccar. Management was comfortable employing a MBB with experience from outside the healthcare sector because the language of Six Sigma is universal and independent of industry type. Red Cross Hospital even received an offer from 3M, a company with a reputation for having successfully implemented Six Sigma, to support it in further developing its Six Sigma organization.

OUTSTANDING RESULTS

The first group of 16 GBs were initially involved with seven projects. One project was terminated during the course of the training because it didn't run well. This was a nice change, because in the pre–Six Sigma phase of the hospital's quality improvement initiative, such a project would have dragged on forever. The other six projects were successfully completed in February 2003. They are described briefly below. More details about these and other projects can be found in a recent article in *Quality and Reliability Engineering International.*[3]

Shortening the length of stay of COPD patients: Patients with chronic obstructive pulmonary disease (COPD) were admitted to either the pulmonary or internal medicine department due to capacity problems in the former. A statistical analysis done by the first team showed a significant difference in the admission time between the two departments. The average stay in the pulmonary department was two days shorter than that in the internal medicine department. A further statistical analysis showed this difference was not due to patient characteristics or physicians. The pulmonary department was just better at treating pulmonary patients.

The hospital rebalanced the bed capacity so all COPD patients could be admitted to the pulmonary department. After this change, inpatient days were saved and more admissions were possible. The annual savings was estimated at $40,000.

Reducing errors in invoices from temp agencies: After an intensive investigation, the second team discovered a considerable number of incorrect invoices from temporary agencies. The errors consistently fell in favor of the agencies and cost the hospital a lot of money to fix. The hospital designed and implemented an improved declaration form that is now required by all agencies contracting with it. In addition to the annual savings estimated at $75,000, Red Cross Hospital experienced a one-time savings of $35,000 due to a refund from the agencies.

Revision of the terms of payment: An analysis by the third team revealed the hospital's suppliers were paid under a variety of terms due to the lack of a uniform payment policy. A standard policy was established, and a number of improvements were implemented. The total savings so far is $35,000 and continues to increase.

Reducing the number of mistakes in invoices: Red Cross Hospital issues 250,000 invoices to patients and insurance companies a year. The fourth team discovered 9% of the invoices were refused and sent back due to the hospital's mistakes. Given the large number of invoices and mistakes, the true statistics lovers saw their finest hour during this project. More than 100 percentage points of improvement were identified, a number of which are still being worked on today. At this time, less than 1% of the invoices are refused, and the savings has exceeded $200,000.

Rooming-in in the children's department: A data analysis done by the fifth team revealed a child's length of stay decreased when parents were permitted to stay with their hospitalized children overnight. Measures were then implemented to facilitate the presence of parents. Armed with the data, insurance companies agreed to pay 80% of the cost for the extra services. The significant decrease in the number of admission days allowed the hospital to admit more children and boost its revenue. The total annual savings was estimated to be about $30,000.

Reducing the number of patients on intravenous antibiotics: Intravenous antibiotics are much more expensive than oral medication. The sixth team found a number of patients who used intravenous antibiotics could have been transferred to oral medication earlier than they were. An analysis showed the internal medicine department was better than the surgical department at managing this process. Further analysis revealed the internal medicine department had a strictly followed standard operating procedure (SOP) for switching between intravenous and oral medication, and the surgical department did not have an SOP. The protocol developed and used by the internal medicine department was adopted as the SOP throughout the hospital. The total annual savings was estimated at $25,000.

Although each of these savings individually may seem relatively modest, they added up to a significant amount. Each required only minor changes and adjustments to the operation and management of the hospital, and more importantly, all the improvement projects provided significant but less tangible benefits to the hospital's management and its customers—the patients.

The six improvement projects illustrate that a $25,000 minimum level of revenue per project can easily be met, and much larger amounts are also possible. Projects in patient care and the administrative departments are also feasible. Because employees are free to suggest ideas for projects, management expects that an improved selection of projects will further enhance revenue in the future.

The results at Red Cross Hospital are encouraging. The hospital's management experienced no significant problems implementing Six Sigma in the nonprofit service organization, and employees were enthusiastic and considered its use a major advantage in managing and executing improvement projects. There is no doubt Red Cross Hospital will continue to use Six Sigma and ISO 9000 as the core of its quality management system.

Acknowledgments

The work described in this article was supported by Red Cross Hospital, the Institute for Business and Industrial Statistics at the University of Amsterdam, the Isenberg School of Management at the University of Massachusetts Amherst and the European Community (EC) through the Thematic Network-Pro-ENBIS-EC (contract number G6RT-CT-2001-05059).

References

1. Mikel Harry, *The Vision of Six Sigma,* Tri Star, 1997.
2. Greg Stock, "Taking Performance to a Higher Level," *Six Sigma Forum Magazine,* Vol. 1, No. 3, pp. 23–26.
3. Jaap van den Heuvel, Ronald J.M.M. Does and M.B. Vermaat, "Six Sigma in a Dutch Hospital: Does It Work in the Nursing Department?" *Quality and Reliability Engineering International,* Vol. 20, No. 5, pp. 419–426.

Bibliography

Barry, Robert, A.C. Murcko and C.E. Brubaker, *The Six Sigma Book for Healthcare,* Health Administration Press, 2002.
Does, Ronald J.M.M., Edwin R. Van den Heuvel, Jeroen De Mast and Søren Bisgaard, "Comparing Nonmanufacturing with Traditional Applications of Six Sigma," *Quality Engineering,* Vol. 15, No. 1, pp. 177–182.
General Electric's Web site, www.gehealthcare.com/prod_sol/hcare/sixsigma.
iSixSigma's Web site, http://healthcare.isixsigma.com.
Kabcenell, Andrea, and Donald W. Berwick, "Pursuing Perfection in Healthcare," *Six Sigma Forum Magazine,* Vol. 1, No. 3, pp. 18–22.
Stahl, Richard, MD, Bradley Schultz and Carolyn Pexton, "Healthcare's Horizon," *Six Sigma Forum Magazine,* Vol. 2, No. 2, pp. 17–26.

A Quest for Quality

Rosanne Zimmerman, Rhonda Smith, Christopher M. B. Fernandes, MD, Teresa Smith, and Ayad Al darrab, MD

IN 50 WORDS OR LESS

- Quality facilitators can plan, organize and move improvement initiatives forward in emergency departments (EDs) with limited resources.

- A multisite teaching hospital used quality facilitators in six quality improvement projects.

- The ED improved patient care and safety, and the staff applied its training to future projects.

Diminishing resources and an increase in patient volume have severely impacted the ability of hospital emergency departments (EDs) to work toward continuous quality improvement (CQI). According to an article in *Quality Management in Health Care*, "Quality improvement is a leading approach to the difficult yet inevitable task of managing organizational change."[1] Though you would be hard pressed to deny the importance of CQI, the lack of both human and financial resources often makes it an unachievable goal.

Although pockets of quality excellence exist in most organizations, others still need a support and resource that team members can access to develop their quality improvement knowledge and skills. A quality facilitator is "a person who has developed special expertise in the CQI process. In a CQI team, the facilitator or advisor is not a team member but a person outside the group who serves as a process guide, teacher of CQI methods and consultant to the team leader, who helps connect the work of the team to the organization's overall CQI effort."[2] Quality facilitators can provide the resources needed to plan, organize and move quality initiatives forward in the ED.

Reprinted with permission from Rosanne Zimmerman, Rhonda Smith, Christopher M. B. Fernandes, Teresa Smith, and Ayad Al darrab, "A Quest for Quality," *Quality Progress* (March 2006): 41–46.

Hamilton Health Sciences, a multisite Canadian healthcare organization with a three-site emergency room program, used quality facilitators in six CQI projects over the course of one year.

THE QUEST STRATEGY

The quality facilitators at Hamilton Health Sciences were called QUEST (quality, utilization, evaluation and safety team) facilitators. Six facilitators covered four hospital sites in a 1000-bed acute care facility. The first placement of QUEST facilitators within the organization occurred when two were assigned to an ED program for one year. This particular ED was chosen, in part, because it had received accreditation recommendations for some specific quality project work and had a committed leadership team.

This ED was also designated an innovation and learning center—an area with a strategic need or stated commitment to move forward with quality initiatives within Hamilton Health Sciences' quality framework. The goals for this center were twofold:

1. To recognize the quality work already in place, build on and support this work and assist with the planning and implementation of new projects.

2. To provide CQI education for all staff involved in the projects and simultaneously develop the CQI experience of the facilitators. This ensured staff developed CQI skills that would transfer to future projects after the QUEST team moved on to support another innovation and learning center.

To develop the strategy, the QUEST team met with the ED leadership team, specifically the chief of emergency medicine and the director of emergency care. This group reviewed a list of 20 current or planned CQI projects and chose six.

The decision of which projects to support was based on several factors. Projects needed to fit into the organizational priority initiatives for quality, including patient safety, patient centered care, appropriateness of care and a healthy work environment. The group also considered the current status of projects, resources available and ED goals.

A contract outlining the expectations of both the QUEST team and the ED was then developed to ensure shared learning.[3] The facilitators developed clear role expectations of leaders and facilitators, created high-level work plans for each project and worked with the leadership team to identify team members for each project. Each project was supported by a multidisciplinary team of employees from management to the front line. The leadership team also made a clear commitment to meet weekly with the facilitators to review progress, provide feedback and support all projects and the frontline staff.

Of all the available facilitation models, the QUEST team chose to use a hybrid that "aim[ed] to balance the achievement of goals with the development of individual and group processes."[4] The team members agreed to combine a philosophy of learning with facilitation of the group's CQI goals. The team decided to provide experiential learning of CQI problem-solving models, processes and tools as well as commit to apply best practices for group processes and meeting management.

The level of support each project received was determined by the work already in progress in the ED and the stage the work was at when the facilitators joined the team. The projects involved assisting with entire project management, evaluating recent department initiatives and building on that information and assisting with data collection to provide information to understand the scope of projects.

THREE CQI MODELS

Each project was based on a CQI model, which provided a unified framework to guide the effort and included the planning, implementation and evaluation of quality projects.[5] Three different models were applied to different projects:

1. Joseph M. Juran's four-step model: project definition, diagnostic journey, remedial journey and holding the gains.

2. The FOCUS plan–do–check–act (PDCA) model, in which FOCUS stands for find a problem, organize a team, clarify current knowledge of the process, uncover the root cause or variation and select the process improvement.[6]

3. The Langley model, which is based on the PDCA framework and includes three grounding questions: What are we trying to accomplish? How will we know the change is an improvement? What changes will result in an improvement?[7]

The use of different models in this setting helped the QUEST facilitators determine which models worked best for different projects, staff members and CQI processes.

Each QUEST meeting started with a "regrounding in quality" agenda item in which the model being used for that particular project was presented to the team and the members discussed where they were in the process and what their next steps were going to be. This strategy helped reinforce CQI learning and application.

THE PROJECTS

Of the six projects, two involved short-term support because they were designed to evaluate the fast track (an area within the ED that treats only nonurgent patients) and changes to the ED X-ray processes, both of which were instituted to improve access and speed of care.

The other four projects aimed to reduce overcrowding by decreasing the length of stay of ED patients, improve the care of acute myocardial infarction patients, improve the care of elderly long-term patients in the ED and improve the triage process to enhance patient safety. All four projects were large in scope and led to multiple system changes.

ROLE OF THE FACILITATOR

Each facilitator was involved in project planning and coordination. This gave senior leaders the time needed to be involved in and lead all the projects without becoming entangled in the background work. It also helped frontline staff feel supported and valued in the project work and gave teams the autonomy to make decisions and act on them.

The facilitators planned all meetings and led teams through the application of the quality tools. They helped team members develop team-building skills, increased learning about best practices for group processes and assisted with implementing change. The facilitators taught short sessions about concepts and tools but mostly relied on team members to learn from the actual application of tools.

RESULTS

The role of the QUEST facilitators proved successful—this ED program moved six projects forward within a year and made some measurable improvements along the way. Table 1 outlines three project initiatives and their outcomes.

Each project group was asked to evaluate how well the QUEST facilitator supported its CQI work. Of the 68% of team members who completed the questionnaires:

- 98% said the role of the QUEST facilitator would be valuable in future projects.

- 92% said this project format led to a team-building environment.

- 98% felt valued by leadership.

- 92% felt valued by the team overall.

- 88% would use a CQI improvement model and best practices for group processes, such as ground rules, consistent meeting evaluations and detailed, goal oriented agendas, in future project work.

Table 1   Summary of continuous quality improvement project results.

Problem	Current performance	Improvement initiatives	Post intervention performance (1 year later)
Inconsistent application of armband for patient identification—patient safety risk.	83% compliance (95% CI: 77–89*).	• Armband applied by business clerk on admission. • Monthly posted armband audits. • Follow-up education sessions for noncompliance.	98% compliance (95% CI: 94–99).
Inconsistent completion of full vital signs (VS) on triage—lack of full assessment of VS was a patient safety risk.	66% compliance (95% CI: 62–70).	• Clear written policy of expectations for VS. • Streamlined triage process. • Increased availability of equipment. • Dedicated triage nurse.	74% compliance (95% CI: 70–78).
Long wait times for nonurgent ED patients.	Average wait time for nonurgent patients = 1.75 hours (95% CI: 1.34–2.19); 4% of patients left without being seen.	Opened fast-track clinic.	Wait times for non-urgent patients = 1.23 hours (95% CI: 0.87–1.59) without a significant impact to urgent patient wait times; 1% of patients left without being seen.

*CI represents the confidence intervals, and the integers represent the upper and lower 95% CI for the compliance.

Several factors made the role of the facilitator a success, but none of it would have been possible without leadership's strong commitment. According to Paul Plsek, "Without strong, effective leadership and an infrastructure to support quality management, improvement efforts may not happen or, if they do happen, may quickly dissipate."[8]

Besides being involved in all project work and providing a visible presence and commitment to the work, senior leaders demonstrated their support in other ways:

- The permission to try new processes and tools allowed the facilitators to apply innovative CQI approaches.

- The expressed recognition and permission to fail and learn provided an environment conducive to innovation.

- The chief of emergency medicine's CQI expertise was a tremendous resource.

- The program director of emergency services supported the frontline staff by enabling them to attend meetings, either by backfilling staff or paying for their time on their days off.

The large scope of the projects chosen and the initiation of QUEST facilitators into this new role led to a decision to involve both facilitators in all projects. This way, they were able to carry a large workload, learn from each other and from each project, develop CQI skills and support one another on the journey. It provided a feedback loop for reflection on facilitation and CQI skills.

Involving both facilitators in all projects also allowed one facilitator to monitor group processes to ensure all members were feeling valued, effectively manage conflict and encourage participation, while the other facilitator moved the project forward and taught CQI principles. This alternating of roles provided an opportunity for the concentrated development of skills and allowed project work to continually move ahead despite illness or vacation schedules. Because of the wealth of experience gained with this strategy, the facilitators in the next innovation and learning center will be able to comfortably move projects forward individually.

An unanticipated positive effect of these projects was that the ED developed strong partnerships with other patient care providers, departments and community partners. Including all key players of a particular process in the CQI team allowed each player to understand the barriers and challenges faced by the other players, and the joint undertaking of the solution built commitment from all sides. These partnerships grew and supported other project work and developed CQI learning beyond the ED.

In an attempt to model the prescribed process of quality, the QUEST facilitators evaluated each CQI meeting based on a number of factors, including:

- Were the meeting goals met?

- Was time used well?

- Were all members equally involved?

- Did all members feel valued?

- Were appropriate decision-making and action plans established?

- Was the meeting effective?

- How well did everyone understand the concepts of quality used in each step of the process?

The facilitators used those evaluations to develop their own skills and determine the need for a change in approach.

All projects were also evaluated by team members at the end of the QUEST project to determine if the project charters were met, to assess the value of the role of the facilitator and to determine what learning took place in relation to CQI and group processes.

LESSONS LEARNED

The project team members were part of an experience that not only applied but also provided education about CQI models and tools. They came away with important skills and information to use on future projects and a resource to contact for further guidance. They also learned how to structure future projects by becoming familiar with some group processes, such as creating purposeful agendas, taking minutes, setting ground rules and completing meeting evaluations.

Other important lessons were learned along the way. The sustainability of project work needs to be carefully considered. Although all project work continued when the QUEST facilitators moved to another innovation and learning center, some team members felt abandoned. In the future, clear timelines and roles will need to be established and reinforced to support members' fears of sustainability once the facilitators leave.

To ensure that future project work will comfortably continue, the QUEST team plans to mentor and coach one or two individuals from the project team in the development of their facilitation and project planning skills. Such individuals will be either frontline staff members or the most appropriate people with high levels of interest, enthusiasm and informal leadership skills. By involving process users in the process, these individuals will build a feeling of value and commitment to future initiatives.

The QUEST team also discovered that simply learning about and applying CQI tools is not enough to build confidence. Compiling a workbook of all tools and processes would have been helpful—in fact, 65% of the members identified it as a need.

Such a workbook would include descriptions of the CQI models and one- to two-page resource guides for each quality tool used, including flowcharts, root cause analyses, affinity diagrams and project charters. For each tool, the book would contain a definition, guidance on when to use it and the steps involved in using it. Group process tools, such as running effective meetings, creating agendas and setting ground rules, would also be included.

The one-year timeline allowed the facilitators time to determine the benefits of some tools over others in terms of results and ease of use. While Juran's model used language that was somewhat familiar to the clinical team members, many believed the simple language of Langley's model was easier to follow.

One final lesson learned is that multiple projects completed in one area in a parallel fashion can lead to human, time and energy exhaustion. Staggered or serial project work with different staff supporting each project will assist with buy-in, spread and sustainability. It will also lessen the strain on resource allocation.

QUEST facilitators provide a way to support CQI initiatives in spite of today's healthcare challenges. To succeed, an organization needs to carefully consider the projects' sustainability and gather support and commitment from its leaders.

References

1. Johan Thor, Karin Wittlov, Bo Herrlin, Mats Brommels, Olle Svensson, John Skar and John Ovretveit, "Learning Helpers: How They Facilitated Improvement and Improved Facilitation—Lessons from a Hospitalwide Quality Improvement Initiative," *Quality Management in Health Care,* Vol. 13, No. 1, 2004, pp. 60–74.
2. M.J. Shamp, "Total Quality Management Glossary," 2004, http://quality.org/ TQM-MSI/TQM-glossary.html (case sensitive).
3. Peter Block, *Flawless Consulting: A Guide to Getting Your Expertise Used,* second edition, Pfeiffer, 1999.
4. Gill Harvey, Alison Loftus-Hills, Jo Rycroft-Malone, Angie Titchen, Alison Kitson, Brendon McCormack and Kate Seers, "Getting Evidence into

Practice: The Role and Function of Facilitation," *Journal of Advanced Nursing,* Vol. 37, No. 6, 2002, pp. 577- 588.

5. Paul Plsek and Nancy Graham, eds., "Tutorial: Quality Improvement Project Models," in *Quality in Health Care: Theory, Application and Evaluation,* Aspen Publishers, 1993.

6. Ibid.

7. Gerald Langley, Kevin Nolan, Thomas Nolan, Clifford Norman and Lloyd Provost, *The Improvement Guide: A Practical Approach to Enhancing Organizational Performance,* Jossey-Bass, 1996.

8. Plsek and Graham, "Tutorial: Quality Improvement Project Models," see reference 5.

Rosanne Zimmerman is a patient safety specialist at Hamilton Health Sciences in Hamilton, Ontario. She earned a master's degree in education from Brock University, St. Catharines, Ontario.

Rhonda Smith is a quality improvement specialist at Hamilton Health Sciences in Hamilton, Ontario. She earned a master's degree in education from Brock University, St. Catharines, Ontario.

Christopher M. B. Fernandes, MD, is a professor and head of emergency medicine at McMaster University in Hamilton, Ontario. He earned his medical degree from the University of British Columbia and is a senior member of ASQ.

Teresa Smith is assistant vice president of the clinical appropriateness and efficiency program at Hamilton Health Sciences in Hamilton, Ontario. She earned an MBA from McMaster University in Hamilton, Ontario.

Ayad Al darrab, MD, is a physician at McMaster University in Hamilton, Ontario. He also earned his medical degree from McMaster University.

Taking Performance to a Higher Level

How Six Sigma Helped a Rural Hospital Achieve a Cultural Transformation

Greg Stock, Thibodaux Regional Medical Center

B ig changes don't necessarily come in big packages. This is especially true for Thibodaux Regional Medical Center, a relatively small nonprofit hospital in southern Louisiana. At Thibodaux, we're beginning the second wave of our journey to excellence—a journey that has already produced impressive results in patient satisfaction, cost savings and quality improvement. Six Sigma is one of several breakthrough strategies the hospital implemented at the beginning of this journey more than a year ago. (See the sidebar "Six Sigma at Thibodaux Regional.")

Reaching the highest level of excellence in patient care requires a high-performance culture skilled not only in the practice of medicine but in the kind of problem-solving proficiencies that drive the best performers in the corporate world. As it has done for many other industries and organizations, Six Sigma methodology is helping Thibodaux Regional transform its culture into one that's high performance because it focuses on the customer, targets performance at near perfect levels and creates a basis for solid, data driven accountability.

To anyone familiar with healthcare delivery, the idea of being able to truly transform the culture within a hospital may sound like a daunting, if not impossible, task. But achieving a genuine cultural transformation in healthcare could be the key to solving some of the most basic and difficult problems facing the industry today. In a competitive climate and with the renewed focus on patient safety, simply claiming a culture of caring isn't enough anymore. We have accepted averages as our standard in the healthcare industry for too long. We used to think if we were just a little above or below the national average, we were OK. We have tolerated and even embraced mediocrity. Six Sigma challenges this line of thinking because it raises the bar and requires solid evidence to support change.

Reprinted with permission from Greg Stock, "Taking Performance to a Higher Level," *Six Sigma Forum Magazine* 1, no. 3: 23–26.

SIX SIGMA AT THIBODAUX REGIONAL

Thibodaux Regional Medical Center is a nonprofit, 149-bed hospital that offers a wide array of outpatient and inpatient services. It also has a freestanding cancer center, a cardiovascular center and several ancillary clinics. The Medical Center has approximately 800 employees. By continuously focusing on patient needs and performance improvement efforts, Thibodaux Regional has been ranked in the top 1% of an all-hospital database for patient satisfaction.

Thibodaux Regional began implementing Six Sigma methodology and training by working with the healthcare services group at GE Medical Systems. The process began with senior leadership sessions and Green Belt (GB) training.

Six GB projects are currently under way at Thibodaux Regional in the areas of accounts receivable days, medication management, patient safety, employee satisfaction, hospital acquired infections and materials management. Training is ongoing for a core team of 18 GBs, and the second wave of Six Sigma foundations training is under way for approximately 30 middle managers and other staff.

Table 1 Thibodaux Regional's pillars of excellence and the Six Sigma related projects.

Pillar	Six Sigma application
Service	Patient satisfaction (ambulatory care unit/emergency department)
Finance	Cycle times (accounts receivable days and accounts payable)
Quality	Reduce defects (medication management)
People	Increased yield and productivity (catheterization lab scheduling)
Growth	All teams through increasing satisfaction, quality and revenue

When Thibodaux Regional began its Six Sigma training in 2000 (with GE Medical Systems), projects were selected based on their alignment with the hospital's strategic plan, their impact on key result areas or pillars of excellence (see Table 1) and their impact on customer and stakeholder key requirements.

REFOCUSING ON THE CUSTOMER

With today's competitive pressures and rising consumerism, hospitals must regain the ability to put the patient at the center of everything they do. Six Sigma helps an institution clearly realize the real reason for its existence by using measurement and analysis to refocus the processes that affect the patient. Focusing on the patient's needs makes good business sense as well, given the strong link between quality and the bottom line.

The initial phase of Six Sigma at Thibodaux Regional was character- ized by the use of patient satisfaction surveys, report cards, statistical tools, interviews, variance reporting, tracking, quality data and other means of quantifying the voice of the customer (patients, physicians, staff). Six Sigma considers what is most critical to quality. Using a step-by-step approach, we were able to separate the critical few factors from the trivial many. We could underscore what was most important to measure, establish or verify a benchmark and actually compare the measurement against the benchmark.

Four of the initial projects chosen directly affected the satisfaction of our customers. The catheterization (cath) lab scheduling project targeted improving physician satisfaction by increasing the number of cases that start on time. A pie chart pointed out the primary reasons for defects that affected the performance of the cath lab and the predictability of the sched- ule (see Figure 1).

After we implemented a pilot phase with a new scheduling format to address the issues causing the defects, physician satisfaction increased

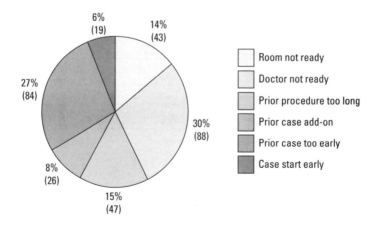

Figure 1 The primary reasons for defects in catheterization lab.

20%. There were significantly fewer complaints by the physicians. The cath lab experienced an increased volume of 29% over the prior year. Under the financial pillar, the additional procedures generated more than $2 million in incremental gross revenue.

COST SAVINGS PROJECTS IMPACT
THE BOTTOM LINE

In the area of cost savings, the accounts receivable project began with the goal of reducing net accounts received to 56 days. Flowcharts and cause-and-effect diagrams helped narrow the project focus (see Figure 2).

To date, project successes include reducing "discharged not final billed" accounts from $3.3 million to less than $600,000 and reducing net accounts receivable from 73.3 to 62.5 days, with an increased cash flow of $2 million per year. This project will continue into the second wave of improvement projects.

In the inventory reduction project, nine teams collected, reviewed and analyzed data to determine areas for improvement that would result in cost

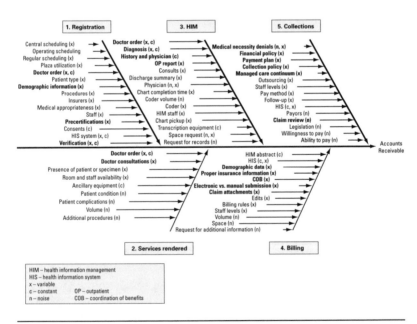

Figure 2 Accounts receivable cause-and-effect diagram.

savings for the hospital. Going forward into the second wave, the teams have thus far demonstrated a savings of more than $450,000 per year. See Table 2 for a list of the target vs. actual savings numbers.

NO COMPROMISE FOR HIGH QUALITY

Even one medication error is too many when it happens at your hospital. The medication management project used statistics to narrow the focus of the project to the order entry or transcription phase (see Table 3). A simple verification system was implemented and piloted, and the pilot was determined to be a success. To date, the project has decreased defects per million opportunities by 42%, a statistically significant number. We have also improved communication between the nurses and pharmacists, and heightened awareness of the importance of the ultimate goal of patient safety. This project will continue in the second wave and focus on the administration phase of the process.

Table 2 Actual savings amounts.

Project	Target	Actual annualized
Supply expense reduction	$150,000	$194,000
Radiology film expense reduction	30,000	55,000
Invoice cycle time	18,000	12,000
General stores/central supply inventory reduction	69,000	57,000
Operating room inventory reduction	262,000	143,000
Inventory carrying costs at 14%	53,000	28,000
Total	**$582,000**	**$489,000**

Table 3 Medication management project—order entry phase.

Order entry	Baseline z-score	Pilot z-score
Total process	4.28	4.45
Omitted	3.81	4.04

TRANSFORMING THE CULTURE

Getting a hospital or health system to perform at the highest level requires a cultural transformation, and making that transformation a reality relies on assigning and accepting responsibility. Six Sigma provides a strong foundation for building data driven accountability. Too often, our evaluation of a process has been based on intuition, assumptions, hearsay, and inaccurate, incomplete or unreliable information. As a result, inefficiencies remain, patient complaints persist, the organization's image suffers and market share is lost.

With Six Sigma, however, Green Belts, process owners and team members immediately recognize an existing process is not working and determine what steps should be taken to fix the problem so it doesn't recur. At Thibodaux Regional, our approach to Six Sigma deployment includes a method for accelerating change by creating a shared need and making sure everyone has a stake in the overall success of our efforts. To really have a lasting impact on the organization, it takes a strategic combination of forces. We bring together both the statistical rigor of Six Sigma and the strength of acceptance-building programs—these programs use the change accelerated process to build buy-in and support.

Though one of the most effective strategies available today, Six Sigma works only when leaders champion the cause. If not acted upon, Six Sigma will be viewed as another program of the month, and those who have introduced it will lose credibility with their associates. Perhaps most unfortunate is that such a lost opportunity will make it more difficult to realize the lofty goals most hospitals espouse in their mission, vision and values statements.

To thrive in a competitive market, healthcare organizations will need to establish an edge—something that sets them apart as industry leaders. Six Sigma is a bold program that illustrates a willingness to go the extra mile when it comes to quality and process improvement. It's the antidote for complacency, and the kind of initiative that helps organizations secure market leadership and gain recognition as top performers.

Six Sigma brings to the healthcare industry a balanced dose of both art and science to improve the delivery of patient care and achieve cultural transformation. It's an approach that enables providers to build acceptance and accountability, develop unique problem-solving skills and link efforts to well-defined organizational objectives. The acquisition of such fundamental capabilities could be the key to success for the industry as a whole. At Thibodaux Regional, our journey to excellence continues with the pursuit of Six Sigma in patient satisfaction, cost savings and quality.

Engaging Physicians In Lean Six Sigma

Chip Caldwell, Jim Brexler, and Tom Gillem

IN 50 WORDS OR LESS

- Participation and support from physicians is crucial in healthcare improvement efforts.

- If they want to engage physicians, hospital administrators must show how improvement projects benefit the doctors.

It may go without saying that healthcare is one of the most complicated industries in which to build quality systems.

That's why most Six Sigma Black Belts (BBs) from outside healthcare fail, after initially saying all industries are alike in that they all manage processes. While this is, of course, true, these BBs quickly become frustrated because of the confusing role of physicians. In fact, in constructing a simple supplier–inputs–processes–outputs–customer diagram, attempting to place physicians in their proper role can cause headaches. Yet, only a handful of process changes can be fully optimized without physician engagement, and active management of the role of physicians may be one of the most vital tasks of senior leaders.

CASE ONE—PHYSICIAN LEADERSHIP

The emergency department (ED) at Morton Plant Medical Center in Clearwater, Florida, faced an unreasonable number of patients leaving without treatment, leading to more than $5 million in lost revenue and causing patient satisfaction scores just above the 60th percentile. Furthermore,

Reprinted with permission from Chip Caldwell, Jim Brexler, and Tom Gillem, "Engaging Physicians in Lean Six Sigma," *Quality Progress* 11 (2005): 42–46. This article is adapted from chapter seven of *Lean-Six Sigma for Healthcare,* published by ASQ Quality Press.

the relationships among ED nurses, inpatient unit nurses, ED physicians and other caregivers were constantly under stress, at one point resulting in a finger-pointing session between ED nurses and ED physicians regarding who was to blame.

Chartered by the CEO and chief nursing executive (CNO), physician director Brian Cook, MD, and nursing manager Donna Moran formed a define, measure, analyze, improve, control (DMAIC) team, composed of four 100-day workout teams focusing on specific ED subprocesses. The 100-day workout is an execution oriented method that lays out a project over the course of 100 days, with prework, a kickoff and 30-day check-ins.

From the outset, Cook clearly established leadership, devoting significant time to reviewing data with subteam leaders, coaching them in developing 100-day workout action plans and overseeing rapid implementation of committed tasks. He resolved internal and external barriers to suggested process pilots by meeting with inpatient unit nurse managers, ancillary department directors, physician leaders and other stakeholders to communicate the ED's goals and routes of collaboration by those in the care stream.

Within a year, ED patient satisfaction saw a 50% gain and topped the 90th percentile, ED length of stay (LOS) dropped 25%, and cost of quality (COQ) recovery exceeded $5 million. So, what did the DMAIC team do to achieve the improvements? They flawlessly executed the following tasks:

- Restated the CEO/CNO vision into ED staff terms.

- Sought statistically valid process drivers around which to craft detailed 100-day workout action plans and appoint team leadership.

- Collaborated with internal and external leaders and stakeholders to set agreed-upon expectations.

- Created the infrastructure to create and track 100-day workout action plans.

- Resolved staff resistance to change, paradigm constraints and delays.

- Led the celebration of achievements and shared praise with all involved.

CASE TWO—MISSED OPPORTUNITIES

A medical center in Mississippi discovered improving care of patients with heart failure and shock (known as DRG 127) would recover more than

$1 million in COQ. Variation in medication use explained almost 90% of variation in cost, as shown in Figure 1.

Further analysis demonstrated that, as shown in Figure 2, adequate variation in medication use warranted an attempt at uncovering sources of variation and engaging key stakeholders in aggressive action.

Administration formed a DMAIC team, which analyzed medications used in great detail and discussed project success factors and risk factors.

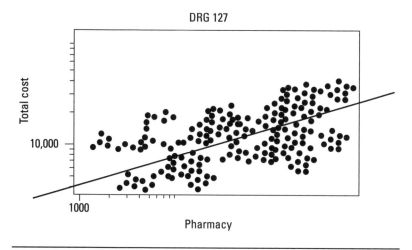

Figure 1 Comparison of total cost to pharmacy cost.

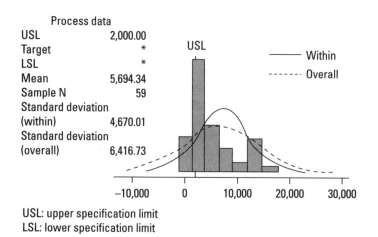

Figure 2 Drug cost distribution.

Table 1   Stakeholder buy-in analysis.

Level of commitment	Physician	Case manager	Pharmacist
Enthusiastic support	●	●	●
Help it work			
Agree		■	
Hesitant			
Indifferent	■		
Opposed			
Hostile			
Not currently involved			■

They concluded, as shown in Table 1, that three critical groups of people would drive the success of reducing variation in medication use—physicians, case managers and pharmacists. Although clinical pharmacists were actively involved in care processes, they had resisted being involved in clinical cost management activities, and case manager involvement had until this point focused on discharge management, not clinical use. However, managers for pharmacy and case management said their staffs would engage if the physicians were engaged.

The chief medical officer agreed with the team that the leading admitter, who was also the informal physician leader, would be best at leading the DMAIC team. When he was approached, his general reaction was positive, and he asked for examples of standing orders and protocols from other organizations with less variation. Several physicians were asked to attend an initial meeting. A second meeting produced a pilot standing order to be suggested to those physicians treating a high number of DRG 127 patients.

After more than six meetings held over six months, almost no physicians, including the physicians authoring the standing order, had used the protocol. The physician leader said many improvements were more important than medication use in DRG 127 and this project was unworthy of additional time and energy. The hospital recovered none of the more than $1 million opportunity.

CASE THREE—OVER BEFORE IT STARTS

A leading academic center in Florida determined ED length of stay (LOS) improvement would yield more than $5 million in reduced nurse worked hours per ED visit and reclaimed patients who were leaving before completing treatment. Based on analysis of ED data, the physician and nurse managers charted a three-pronged approach to reduce ED LOS, as follows:

1. Reduce bottlenecks and delays in flow, particularly time to ED bed and time from ED physician initial assessment to request for inpatient bed.

2. Reduce 50% of the variation in nurse staffing to hour-by-hour patient demand.

3. Reduce 50% of the variation in ED physician LOS variation.

The analysis of physician variation found significant unexplained differences in clinical practice, as illustrated in Figure 3.

At the initial meeting, a general apathy and resentment was apparent among most physicians. One of the more respected physicians said it was unimportant how long the patient stayed. Also, in many cases, she ordered a lot of tests unrelated to the patient's primary complaint because many patients did not have adequate primary care and she believed quality care required her to order preventive tests. She went on to advise her colleagues that if the medical center prevented her from this primary physician role in conducting her ED physician episodic care duties, she might be forced to find work at a hospital that valued "quality" care.

Despite this initial setback, a second meeting was planned, but the emergency physician manager rescheduled it at the last minute to be held 30 days later. A week before this meeting, he cancelled it again.

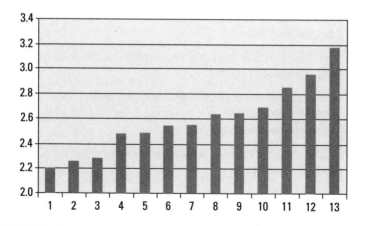

Figure 3 Emergency department physician length of stay variation.

REASONS FOR RESISTANCE

Although physicians are indeed part of the healthcare system managed by the medical center, this fact is often not recognized. Some physicians even resist the notion that their actions affect other processes in the system, such as nursing, pharmacy, medical records or billing and collections. Many are aware of the effect of their processes on medical center processes but prefer to ignore it.

However, one important reason physicians resist change is that the change frequently places more burden on their processes—consuming more time, increasing complexity and providing less service to them or their patients. It is often the case that medical center leaders do not fully understand the physicians' processes before brainstorming potential changes. As a first step, leaders can go a long way toward averting resistance by simply developing what W. Edwards Deming called "profound knowledge" of physicians' processes in the DMAIC analyze phase before entering the improve phase.

The reasons for the physicians' reactions in cases two and three could be varied and complex. However, by and large, disengagement by physicians in organizationwide improvement efforts can be attributed to relatively few causes, as follows:

1. Not vested in the intended outcome.[1]

2. Not understanding systems thinking or process analysis.

3. A bias that more resources and more staff are the best solutions and detailed analysis is a waste of time.

4. Adverse effect on physician processes by processes that aid hospital improvement.

5. A stance that they should be compensated for their activities benefiting the hospital.

6. A stance that the priority should be to improve processes that benefit their practices in the hospital before the hospital benefits from bottom-line improvements.

7. Little consensus among physicians regarding priority focus areas or their solutions.

8. A lack of teamwork in physician behavior patterns, even if the individual practice is within the same medical group.

THE HEALING PROCESS

How can healthcare leaders tip the scale toward more effective collaboration and engagement from physicians? The most effective approaches to engage physicians seem to be to:

- Seek to fully understand physician needs in general and within the specific process to be changed during the prework, define and improve phases of a DMAIC project and learn the degree of support required. A useful tool for analyzing physician and other key stakeholder current and required positions regarding the change is shown in Table 1.

- Seek to build trust. This probably sounds simple, but trust between the physician and the hospital executive has dramatically eroded over the past decade. The reasons can be complex or simple. In many cases, in the quest to recover lost margins, executive teams have sometimes flown in the face of physician interests and desires. As a result, the collaborative model has deteriorated to a combative level.

- Educate physicians in all aspects of healthcare management, financial management, regulatory environment and competitive pressures with an aim to establish a true visioning partnership about the future (not just cursory staff meeting advisories of days gone by).[2]

- Seek win–win projects. That is, find projects that will delight physicians, usually by improving the efficiency in physician–hospital interfacing processes. For example, a significant long-term goal in surgery, assigned to the CNO, would be to increase the ratio of "cut to close" hours (hours that patients are in surgery) per week and total nursing hours per week. In most surgery units, cut to close hours make up about 50% of the total nursing hours for a week, meaning the other half of the time, nurses are on duty but not in surgery. By increasing the ratio, nursing hours are being better used—more hours are spent in surgery than out of surgery.

This can be accomplished by sticking to a strict surgery start time, decreasing case turnaround times and increasing accuracy of physician preference card picking, the process in which surgeons request the instruments they need in the operating room. DMAIC charters to improve each of the processes can be written to support those matters most important to surgeons, that is, reducing their downtime between cases. This will be embraced by surgeons and at the same time reduce COQ, in the form of decreased nurse staffing before and between cases.

- Negotiate a quid pro quo, in which the organization provides a concession in some other area in exchange for physician agreement to embrace the desired change.

- Seek physician influencers (referrers, physicians with high credibility) to lead the way, instead of hospital managers and executives.

- Integrate improvement work casually into existing physician committee and task force structures by replacing those agenda items that are discussion oriented, nonaction-producing topics and scheduling Joint Commission on Accreditation of Healthcare Organizations topics bimonthly or quarterly instead of monthly (unless mandated) to free up time for action oriented work and follow-up. The 100-day workout action plan format or a modification is ideally suited for action tracking.

- Consider incentives. Although beware: incentives are often effective in the short term, but once offered become expected. Hence, the absence becomes a demotivator.

- Seek nonphysician caregivers to execute the change or influence physicians to embrace the change. For example, since ambulation on the first postoperative day is a statistically significant driver for patients receiving hip replacement surgery, physical therapists can be engaged to call surgeons on the day of surgery soliciting a physical therapy order.

RECOMMENDED LEARNING SESSION

Here's a recommended learning session for a one-hour senior leader meeting on engaging physicians. One member of the executive team should serve as the recorder, capturing feedback on a flipchart.

1. Each executive takes 10 minutes to review the list of ways to approach physicians and record opportunities to engage physician

leaders in a current initiative using one or more of the techniques listed (or innovation of a technique not listed).

2. Go around the room, discussing ideas generated by the executive group.

3. Discuss what, if anything, can be done to elevate physician engagement in one or more of the initiatives discussed.

4. Discuss who should act on the engagement ideas discussed. (The recorder or another accountable executive team member should be asked to capture this action plan.)

5. Set aside an hour every one to three months to review the action plan for progress.

These approaches, while not unique, are indeed time-consuming and, thus, are less optimized in many healthcare organizations than is required to fully realize the power of Lean Six Sigma. Heroic process innovation simply can not be realized without physician engagement.

References

1. Michael Cabana, et. al., "Why Don't Physicians Follow Clinical Practice Guidelines?: A Framework for Improvement," *Journal of the American Medical Association,* Vol. 282, No. 15, 1999, pp. 1,458–1,465.
2. Richard W. Schwartz and Kenneth H. Cohn, "The Necessity for Physician Involvement in Strategic Planning in Healthcare Organizations," *The American Journal of Surgery,* Vol. 184, No. 3, 2002, pp. 269–278.

Bibliography

Six Sigma Pocket Guide, Rath and Strong, 2000.

Chip Caldwell is president of Chip Caldwell Associates in Saint Augustine, Florida. He has a master's degree in healthcare management from Central Michigan University in Mount Pleasant, Michigan, and is a member of ASQ.

Jim Brexler is CEO of Erlanger Health Systems in Chattanooga, Tennessee, and a fellow in the American College of Healthcare Executives. He has a master's degree in public affairs from North Carolina State University.

Tom Gillem is vice president of client communications for m21partners, a subsidiary of Management 21 Inc., in Nashville, Tennessee. He earned a master's degree in journalism from Northwestern University in Chicago.

Learning from Mistakes

Hospital Team Discovers Valuable Lessons after TQM Effort Disbands

Diana V. Shaw, Denni O. Day, and Elizabeth Slavinskas

Three years ago, Strong Memorial Hospital in Rochester, New York, adopted the principles and tools of total quality management (TQM) and embarked on a plan to educate 5000 employees by the end of 1997. In early TQM training cycles, trainees worked in teams to identify and solve problems by applying TQM principles and tools. In January 1992, a multidisciplinary team was formed that included representatives from the emergency medicine, neurology, nursing, ophthalmology, social work, and urology departments. The team initially had nine members plus an administrative liaison and a facilitator. Of the nine team members, four were physicians, three were administrators, one was a social work manager and one was a clinical nursing chief.

SETTING THE STAGE

During the 12 months that followed the team's appointment, it used a six-step problem-solving model (see Figure 1). As with any team effort, initial emphasis was placed on creating a cohesive team, which was particularly challenging in this case because the team members were not accustomed to working together and many had never met. Therefore, ground rules were established that would create and maintain an environment conducive to productive team meetings. The team negotiated and agreed on rules that allowed members to begin working and functioning as a cohesive team (see the "Team Ground Rules" sidebar).

IDENTIFYING A UNIVERSAL PROBLEM

Once the ground rules were established, the team moved to problem identification, the first step of the problem-solving process. First, the team

Reprinted with permission from Diana V. Shaw, Denni O. Day, and Elizabeth Slavinskas, "Learning from Mistakes," *Quality Progress* 11 (June 1995): 45–48.

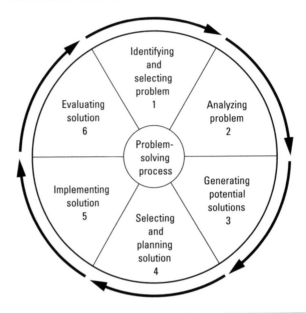

Figure 1   Problem-solving process.

Source: Leadership through Quality, Problem-Solving Process User's Manual, Xerox Corporation, 1986.

needed to define a problem that would apply to all team members. After eight weekly, one-hour meetings, the team agreed on a clinical problem that would require the active support and participation of all team members, especially the clinicians.

The problem selected by the team was the emergency department's difficulty in appropriately identifying and obtaining consultations and referrals. The team's desired outcome was to decrease the number of inappropriate emergency department consultations and referrals and increase the number of appropriate ones.

The team immediately realized that there was no single definition of a consultation or a referral. After much discussion, a consensus was reached: consultation was defined as a request for immediate service from one or more specialists, and a referral was defined as a request for specialty services that could be scheduled for the future.

Once the problem statement was complete, the team had to define the current state and the desired state. The current state was identified as one in which the emergency department requested some consultations that specialists believed were not necessary and didn't request others that specialists believed were necessary. This resulted in a low level of cooperation

---

TEAM GROUND RULES

Call the team leader if you are not able to attend the meeting.

Start the meeting on time.

If you are late or leave early, it is your responsibility to find out what was missed.

Neurology will decide on a representative if the assigned team member cannot attend.

Minutes and the agenda will be distributed with enough lead time so that team members can prepare for the next meeting.

The team will meet in the emergency department conference room every Friday from 2 to 3 p.m.

The meeting will be held if a quorum is present.

It is essential for the designated minute taker and timekeeper to arrive on time and stay for the entire meeting.

Roles will be rotated every two weeks, first as minute taker and then as timekeeper, in alphabetical order.

---

between the specialty departments and the emergency department and a slower-than-desired response time. The desired state, to be achieved by the end of 1992, was defined as one in which appropriate consultations would be requested, increasing consultants' responsiveness.

ANALYZING THE PROBLEM STATEMENT

Analysis of the problem statement, step 2 of the problem-solving process, began with a review of emergency room patient medical records for the most recent week. A representative from each of the clinical areas participating on the team, including the emergency department, reviewed medical records for all patients seen in the emergency department during that week.

Each reviewer independently determined, based only on the documentation, if a consultation or referral should have been requested from a specialty service. Results from all of the reviewers were then analyzed to determine the frequency with which agreement was reached and to compare reviewers' opinions with what actually took place (that is, whether a consultation or referral was requested). This analysis was expected to validate the problem statement, provide data to help the team determine the magnitude of the problem, and identify specific areas where the problem occurred with greater frequency.

As expected, the results of the analysis validated the problem's existence. They also showed that there were differences of opinion between the specialty services and the emergency department medical staff. Team discussions, however, revealed that the actual data collection process had not proceeded in the manner originally specified. The emergency department staff had reviewed all patient charts in advance and pulled only those medical records for which consultations were requested or those that they believed required consultations. Only these preselected records were given to the specialty services for their review. While this revised process did allow the degree of agreement between the specialty services and the emergency department to be assessed, the smaller, preselected subset potentially minimized the magnitude of the problem. But, even though the revised process resulted in possibly skewed data and the magnitude of the problem had not been clearly defined, the team decided not to repeat the analysis because sufficient information had been obtained to confirm the existence of a problem.

PROBLEMS, PROBLEMS, PROBLEMS

The team had sporadic participation from many of its members and attempted to deal with this by appointing alternate team members. These alternate members, however, did not have sufficient ownership of the problem and had not participated in the TQM training.

Also, due to turnover, a new team member was added to the team who was not trained in TQM processes and tools. Consequently, the new team member prolonged the team's struggle by questioning the process being used to investigate the problem and develop solutions.

The team's struggle was further exacerbated by some team members wanting to quickly find solutions so they could stop wasting time in meetings.

DIGGING FOR THE ROOT CAUSE

In spite of these difficulties, the team pushed on and, using TQM tools and techniques, systematically identified root causes for the problem of inappropriate consultations. The facilitator guided the team through the development of an affinity diagram and cause-and-effect diagram to help find two root causes: a lack of care standards and conflicting attitudes and expectations of emergency department and specialty service physicians.

The cause-and-effect diagrams also helped the team realize the need for additional data. The team determined that it would be necessary to collect information on attitudes and expectations from others involved in the consultation process, such as nurses, residents and the hospital's paging office. A survey was developed and distributed to nurse practitioners, residents, and attending physicians representing the neurology, ophthalmology, urology and emergency departments. The results of this survey confirmed that the respondents had different perceptions and expectations of the consultation and referral process.

RESOLUTION: DISBAND

During this data collection process, the team continued to struggle with lack of participation and reached a point beyond which progress could not be made. To generate potential solutions to this problem (step 3 of the problem-solving process), the participation of all team members, especially those with clinical expertise, was necessary. Based on their experiences, however, team members believed this level of participation would probably not be achieved. The team members were finally forced to admit that they could not proceed further and agreed to disband.

The lack of resolution was not blamed on individual team members, but on the many outside factors. This outcome could probably be traced to a combination of the following factors:

- The team had been established before any problem was identified, so inappropriate stakeholders might have been named.

- The selected problem might not have been important to all team members.

- The TQM training might have been ineffective or incomplete.

- Untrained team members might have slowed down the rest of the group.

Before the team disbanded, it agreed that data must go to the appropriate service areas for decisions on further action, medical members of the TQM group should further discuss a plan of action, and the emergency department should address the way the phone system and pages are handled.

One item was completed. During the data collection process, the team had discovered improvements that could be made to the way the emergency department was handling pages. Solutions were selected, implemented, and continue to be monitored by the emergency department (steps 4, 5, and 6 of the problem-solving process).

LESSONS LEARNED

The most important outcome of the team effort was not the development and implementation of a solution to the chosen problem, but instead the lessons that were learned about incorporating TQM into traditional problem-solving methods:

1. *Problem identification must precede team formation.* The team was formed as a result of a training process that instructed a group of individuals to identify a problem that affected all team members. This didn't work. Teams should be formed naturally with key stakeholders; this is especially important because TQM requires a great deal of time and effort. Only those who are truly committed to resolving a problem or improving a system will dedicate the necessary time and effort.

2. *The team's mandate must be clarified at the first meeting.* To alleviate unnecessary stress and to avoid unproductive experiences with the TQM problem-solving process, the team's goal must be known from the outset of the project. The hospital team had two purposes: to demonstrate its knowledge of and ability to use TQM principles and tools and to identify and solve a problem that currently existed and affected all team members. Unfortunately, these two purposes couldn't be fulfilled with the force-fit team.

3. *Inexperienced TQM teams require a significant investment of time.* Without a time commitment from all team members, the rate at which progress is made does not merit the time and effort expended. This could result in waning enthusiasm and unproductive efforts, as was the case with this team.

4. *Training in the TQM process is necessary.* Training in the use of TQM tools and techniques can either cover only those topics pertinent to the effort under way or those topics relating to all available TQM tools. In either case, a thorough understanding of and immersion in the TQM philosophy and problem-solving process are essential prior to participation on a TQM team.

Without such a foundation, the team's efforts will be awkward and inefficient, if not unproductive. For example, the hospital team included several untrained members. Without a clear understanding of the structured TQM problem-solving process, the untrained team members often jumped to conclusions and advocated solutions prior to clearly defining the problem.

Occasionally, it might be necessary to include team members who are not trained, but the inclusion of untrained members would only be appropriate if the team agreed that the benefit of adding them to the team outweighed the delays in accomplishing the team's work.

5. *Build team consensus.* The consensus-building process develops interpersonal relationships and allows individuals to function as a team. Even after the team disbands, additional benefits can accrue if these relationships are used to address new issues before they develop into major problems.

   The hospital team's problems with the consensus-building process were apparent in the length of time it took the team to reach consensus on the problem statement and to agree on definitions for consultation and referral.

6. *Identify problems that are best solved using TQM principles.* Since there are some problems that are best solved by making a simple decision, a quick review of the problem-solving steps can help determine whether a TQM team is required. The focus, however, needs to be on the activity or problem being addressed rather than the TQM process itself.

7. *TQM principles and tools should also be used outside the team process.* By using TQM principles and tools in settings other than the team project, a higher level of understanding and proficiency will be reached and continuous improvements can be made, thereby enhancing the organization's quality and efficiency.

8. *Don't jump to solutions.* This lesson is a natural outcome of the structured process encouraged by TQM. When a problem has been identified, early determination of a solution without investigation into the root causes can result in wasted effort and money. The amount and depth of the analysis, however, will depend on the problem itself. The problem-solving process should be used to assess the situation, identify the root causes, and develop subsequent solutions.

9. *Data availability should be assessed and identified early in the process.* Problem verification can be difficult if the team neglects to assess data availability until development of the data collection plan is well under way. Overlooking this important step can waste time and delay or halt the project.

USE TQM TOOLS WITH CARE

TQM can be a powerful process for solving operational problems. As with any management methodology, care should be taken with TQM. While this exciting philosophy offers hope of an improved working environment or the development of a higher-quality product, the hospital team's experience demonstrated that caution must be exercised. Proper training is necessary, and a balance should be found between the application of TQM principles and the magnitude of the problem. The process should not outweigh the goals and objectives, and TQM tools should be used only as needed, with care and wisdom.

Diana V. Shaw is the neurology program administrator at the University of Rochester School of Medicine in New York. She has a master's degree in public health from the University of Rochester School of Medicine.

Denni O. Day is the research administrator for the Movement and Inherited Neurologic Disorders Unit at the University of Rochester Medical Center in New York. She has a master's degree in public health administration from the University of North Carolina at Chapel Hill.

Elizabeth Slavinskas is the clinical nursing chief for emergency and ambulatory care at the University of Rochester Strong Memorial Hospital in New York. She has a master's degree in nursing from the State University of New York at Buffalo.

Part II

Cases and Examples of the Use of Lean Six Sigma in Healthcare

Hospital Reduces Medication Errors Using DMAIC and QFD

Yani Benitez, Leslie Forrester, Carolyn Hurst, and Debra Turpin

---

IN 50 WORDS OR LESS

- An Illinois hospital reduced work while improving process performance 90% during a medication error reduction project.

- A Black Belt helped a multidisciplinary team use Six Sigma's define, measure, analyze, improve and control methodology.

- The team then used quality function deployment to design and develop the process functions.

Trying to improve quality by eliminating process steps might appear to be a contradiction. But this was not the case when a 200-plus full-service hospital in Illinois targeted medication error reduction as a 2005 goal.

In fact, the Joint Commission on Accreditation of Healthcare Organizations (JCAHO)–accredited Alton Memorial Hospital achieved a more than 90% improvement in process performance as a result of the project.

BACKGROUND

Alton Memorial, part of the St. Louis–based BJC HealthCare, naturally supports a culture of patient safety as part of its mission. The Agency for Healthcare Research and Quality estimates the incident rate for an adverse drug event (ADE) at between two and seven per 100 hospital admissions nationwide, with a mean cost of $4,685 per event.[1]

Reprinted with permission from Yani Benitez, Leslie Forrester, Carolyn Hurst, and Debra Turpin, "Hospital Reduces Medication Errors Using DMAIC and QFD," *Quality Progress* (January 2007): 38–45.

At only 0.02%, Alton Memorial's medication error rate was low compared to those nationwide statistics. But the potential cost savings to the institution that would result from even a small improvement in ADEs could not be ignored.

Of those medication errors reported in the hospital's risk management database, 43% were caused by transcription errors. Transcription involves the copying of a physician order for the purpose of processing. The strict guidelines that define a transcription error are based on the National Coordinating Council for Medication Error Reporting and Prevention (NCC MERP) error category index.[2]

Information copied incorrectly or omitted is considered a transcription error. This includes missing, inaccurate or only partially provided special instructions with a physician order. An example of a special instruction is: give only if pain level greater than five one hour after Tylenol.

A multidisciplinary team was formed at the hospital to find ways to reduce the hospital's medication errors. Team members included representatives from pharmacy, nursing, clinical information systems, nursing management, performance improvement and medication safety. Hospital management requested the help of a Six Sigma Black Belt (BB) to guide the team through the process. A BB was assigned to this team in a facilitator and trainer role.

METHODOLOGY

Initially, the team followed a define, measure, analyze, improve and control (DMAIC) methodology. In the define phase the team realized hospital management mandated two distinct goals:

- Reduce the defect rate of the current process with quick-hit initiatives.

- Develop a standardized process that works for all hospital units except the emergency unit (EU), because of the immediate nature of its needs.

With these two goals, the team expected to improve order entry accuracy related to transcription errors by 50%.

In the measure phase, the team flowcharted the current medication order entry processes. The team quickly realized each unit had developed its own medication ordering process. Most used two documents to review each order: the medication administration record (MAR) and a chronological sheet, a tool devised and used only by nursing staff.

The intent of the chronological sheet was twofold:

- Provide a historical list of medications received throughout a patient stay.
- Act as a repeat check against the MAR each shift.

The purpose of this double check system was to help ensure order accuracy. Although the MAR information should have been verified against the physician orders, the staff deemed this step too cumbersome and labor-intensive and created the chronological sheet for nurses to rewrite every medication order by hand.

ELIMINATING A DOCUMENT

It became clear that data needed to be collected to compare the accuracy of the MAR and the chronological sheet. A small baseline study was performed in the third quarter of 2004. The pharmacist's order entry accuracy in the MAR was 95% the first time through, yet once the order was verified by the pharmacist, the pharmacy software and the nursing staff, the MAR accuracy increased to 99.98%.

On the other hand, the chronological sheet was itself fairly inaccurate (10% error rate). Unfortunately, nurses had developed a false sense of security with the chronological sheets, assuming they were correct. Furthermore, this tool was used during the entire patient stay, so mistakes could carry through multiple days.

Concurrently, interpretations of orders, abbreviations and the definition of the policy guidelines had differences between the two forms. These variances were contributing to the frequency and type of transcription errors.

The team concluded the chronological sheet had to be retired because it added no value to medication order entry accuracy. Eliminating it represented an average seven minute workload reduction per patient per day.

REDUCING PHARMACIST INTERRUPTIONS

By analyzing cases, the team identified disruptions to the pharmacist during the order entry process as a repeating cause of mistakes. Actions taken to reduce disruptions included:

- Establishing a process for all intravenous fluid orders to be sent to pharmacy before 6 a.m. daily so they could be prepared early.

- Establishing a missing medication sheet for the clinical units to fax instead of phoning their questions and concerns to the pharmacy. In the pharmacy, a technician would review the request and assess whether it could be handled by someone other than a pharmacist. After completing the order entry for a given patient, the pharmacist then would address the waiting requests prior to starting the order entry for the next patient.

- Training pharmacists on a consistent medication order entry format.

Another cause of transcription errors was the illegibility of the physician order. There was not enough space on the form for physicians to write medication orders, forcing them to write outside the assigned box or in tiny script. This caused multiple issues such as illegible orders, eliminated words and missing information.

Ten more lines were added to the form. Margins were darkened to reduce the possibility of writing outside the faxable area. The guidelines inside the writing area were made to be invisible when faxed to pharmacy. Finally, fax machines were tested and adjusted to improve quality.

These changes improved the medication order entry process, yet the issue of the multiple ways staff processed medication errors remained.

STANDARDIZATION

The team shifted its focus to the second goal: designing one standard medication order process for all hospital units to use, except the EU. The new process had to function flawlessly in such diverse areas as critical care, where patient medications change constantly, and long-term care where patients tend to have a long list of medications.

To achieve this goal, the team decided to follow a design for Six Sigma methodology, quality function deployment (QFD), to link the needs of the customers with the design and development of the process functions. QFD helps organizations identify both spoken and unspoken needs, translate these into actions and designs, and focus various business functions toward achieving this common goal.

The first question to answer was: Who is our customer in the medication order entry process? Even though the ultimate customer is the patient, the primary and more immediate customer was determined to be the nurse in charge of the patient.

The team then set about capturing the voice of the customer (VOC), getting insights into the nurses' needs through interviews. The top needs identified were:

- *Quick access to medication order information.* It should take no more than one minute and three steps to access a patient's medication information.

- *Quick pharmacy turnaround time.* Orders should be entered into the MAR system within 120 minutes. A real-time copy of the order should be available while the order is being entered into the MAR system.

- *The process must provide a history of patient medications.* Nurses should be able to see all medication orders, including start and stop times for the entire patient stay.

- *Information should be portable and mobile.* Nurses should not need to return to the nursing station to learn what medications are due to be administered and when.

- *The new process should provide double-checking capability for MAR information.*

- *Order entry needs to be trustworthy.* It should be at least 95% accurate the first time they are entered in the MAR. Pharmacists should be consistent in the way they enter the order.

A hierarchical value then was assigned to each customer need, representing the relative importance the need had with respect to other needs. For instance, a hierarchical value of 2% can be interpreted as meaning only 2% of the customers considered it important. Table 1 summarizes the results.

The team analyzed the current processes and the perceptions nurses from all units had of each process's effectiveness. The medication order entry process flowchart for each unit also was revisited. Because each unit followed a different order entry process, its evaluation of the current process performance was relative to its own application of it.

The nurses' needs then were converted into quantitative measures of success with established metrics and targets. These would become the design requirements for the new process. Each design requirement was rated against the customer (nurse) needs in terms of the strength of its correlation. The resulting QFD matrix is shown in Figure 1.

ANALYZING OPTIONS

Now that the design requirements had been defined and the nurses' needs measured, the next step was to analyze options. In this phase the team generated alternative concepts of processes that could be designed.

Table 1   Hierarchy of nurses' needs.

Nurses' need	Defined as:	Hierarchy
Quick access	Available immediately for printing (less than one minute).	2%
	Less than three steps to access the document.	2%
Quick pharmacy turnaround time	Less than two hours.	38%
	Fax of order available in real time.	7%
Provide history of meds	Able to see all medications for the entire patient stay.	2%
	Able to see medication start and stop dates.	2%
Portable/mobile	Nurse should not need to go back to station for document.	2%
Check on MAR	Serve to double-check all orders in medication administration record (MAR).	12%
	Medications sort in the same way as MAR.	7%
Trustworthy	At least 95% accurate the first time.	19%
	Consistency in order entry by all pharmacists.	7%

MAR = medication administration record.

These concepts then were evaluated against customer (nurse) needs from Table 1.

Some of the concepts considered were:

1. *Use the existing patient care activity record (PCAR) system as the medication list, with some minor enhancements.* PCAR uses the MAR information to generate its medication list—one source of information. This process already was scheduled to be replaced by an electronic medication bar coding system called the medication administration checking system (MAK), slated for implementation in the fall of 2005.

2. *Deploy the MAK system early.* MAK would detect any discrepancy between the medication and the order at the bedside. It was scheduled for implementation in the fourth quarter of 2005. This proposal called for extra resources to expedite the system's launch by the spring of 2005.

3. *Use optical character recognition (OCR) technology.* OCR equipment scans images of medication orders as they are faxed to the pharmacy. It converts handwriting into electronic lists of medications stored in a folder that is accessible with a mouse click.

Correlation Matrix

	Fax to MAR time	Desktop to document clicks (steps)	MD order availability	Process to enter medication orders	Availability printed copy of document	First pass percentage orders incorrect	First pass number of defects
Fax to MAR line			+	+	+	+	+
Desktop to document					+		
MD order availability							
Process to enter medication					+	+	+
Availability printed copy of document							
First pass percentage orders incomplete							++
First pass number of defects							

	Customer requirements / Design requirements	Importance	Fax to MAR time	Desktop to document clicks (steps)	MD order availability	Process to enter medication orders	Availability printed copy of document	First pass percentage orders incorrect	First pass number of defects	Customer rating: 1 = worst	2	3	4	5 = best
	Direction of improvement		↓	↓	Ω	Ω	Ω	↓	↓					
Quick access	Available immediately for printing	3	9	3	1	1							@ x	#
	Less than three steps to access the document	3	3	9		1	1						@	x#
Quick pharmacy turnaround time (TAT)	Quick TAT	50	9	1	3	9	3	3	3	@ x	#			
	Facsimile of order available in real time	10	3		9	3	1	3	3	@ x		#		
Provide history of medications	Able to see all meds for the entire patient stay	3	3	1	3	9	1	1	1			@		x#
	Able to see med start and stop dates	3	3	1	3	9	1	1	1			x	@#	
Portable/mobile	Nurse should not need to go back to station for document	3		1	1		9	1	1		x	#		@
Check on MAR	Serve to double-check all orders in MAR	15	3	1	3	9	3	1	1			x#		@
	Medications sort in the same way as MAR	10	3			9	3	1	1			@x#		
Trustworthy	At least 95% accurate the first time	25	3	1	1	3		9	9	@	#	x		
	Consistency in order entry by all pharmacists	10	3	1	1	9		9	9	@	#	x		
Technical importance	Absolute		714	145	344	930	271	529	529					
	Relative (percentage)		21	4	10	27	8	15	15					

MAR = medication administration record, @ = in-patient unit, x = labor and delivery, # = long-term care.

Figure 1 Quality function deployment matrix.

A Pugh selection matrix was used to evaluate these concepts against customer (nurse) needs.[3] The Pugh matrix compares multiple concepts against a baseline model in terms of how well they address VOC. The preferred concept can be either the one with the highest number of plus signs minus the number of minus signs or a new concept that incorporates superior characteristics of the proposed concept ideas.

Based on the Pugh matrix results in Figure 2, the team decided to implement the PCAR option because it had the lowest number of minus signs, same number of plus signs as MAK, yet was very easy to test and could be implemented quickly.

Option two, MAK, would have required significant hardware and structural changes to the way medication is ordered and delivered. More lead time was required than was available. The OCR technology requires the purchase of hardware. There also were reliability and capability concerns regarding its ability to read physicians' handwriting.

		Concepts				
			Current process (chronology)	Existing patient care activity record	Medication administration checking system (MAK)	Optical character recognition
Criteria	Available immediately for printing.	**Datum (baseline)**		S	–	S
	Less than three steps to access the document.			S	S	S
	Quick turnaround time.			S	S	S
	Facsimile of order available in real time.			S	S	S
	Able to see all medications for the entire patient stay.			–	–	–
	Able to see medication start and stop dates.			S	S	S
	Nurse should not need to go back to station for document.			S	S	–
	Serve to double-check all orders in MAR.			S	S	+
	Medications sort in the same way as in MAR.			+	+	–
	At least 95% accurate the first time.			+	+	+
	Consistency in order entry by all pharmacists.			+	+	+
	Total +			3	3	3
	Total –			1	2	3

+ = Better than datum
– = Worse than datum
S = Same as datum

Figure 2 Pugh selection matrix.

GOING LIVE

The team discussed verification plans, including a pilot program. A go-live date of April 4 was selected because of the usual low patient census on Sunday nights. Mandatory training sessions were programmed throughout the month of March to educate nursing staff on the new process.

On April 3, the team performed a second hospitalwide baseline study to reassess the accuracy of the current process. For simplicity's sake, the metric used was errors per bed instead of the more representative errors per order. The resulting baseline value was 0.4 errors per bed, a value similar to the results of the initial baseline study conducted at the beginning of the project, which yielded 90% accuracy per order or 0.5 errors per bed.

At midnight, the chronological sheet was removed from all patient charts and the PCAR process was put into place. During the day the team surveyed all units, answered questions, gathered feedback and supported the nurses throughout the transition.

The new process uses the physician orders as the double check for the MAR accuracy. When a new medication order is written, the nurse keeps the information in the PCAR. Once pharmacy enters the order into the MAR, the nurse verifies it against what was in the PCAR and signs off the orders as entered in the MAR. In case of discrepancy, the nurse goes back to the physician for verification. Any changes are recorded in the MAR and corrected in the PCAR on the next printout.

Of course, the keystone of the PCAR initiative's success is for staff to actually verify new medication orders in the computer before signing off on them. This process was not happening with the chronological sheet, thus mistakes could remain undetected for multiple days.

The PCAR process is quite similar to the process required by the new MAK. Starting it now would allow for a seamless transition to MAK later.

RESULTS

A control plan was developed to collect data on the current process and ensure the improvements are maintained over the long term. The plan addresses issues regarding the type of random audits to perform, by whom, how often and the reaction plan if the process goes out of control.

These random audits are conducted weekly by the medication safety officer. An average of 30 chart audits are completed per week based on individual nursing unit census. The results of the audits are shown in a control chart (see Figure 3).

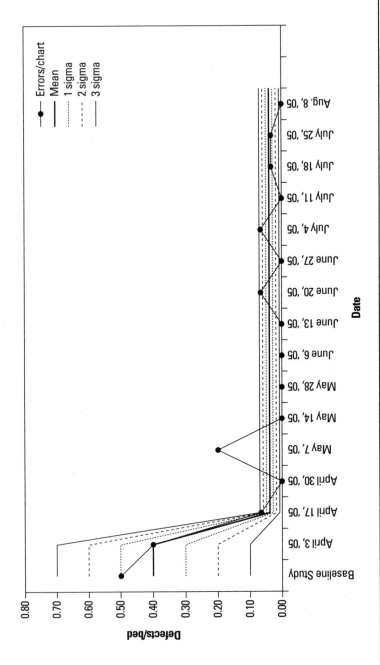

Figure 3 Control chart of medical transcription errors per bed.

The control chart allows the process owner to monitor changes in medication errors by distinguishing random day-to-day variation from variation caused by a significant change in process performance. In the control chart the average weekly errors per bed is plotted against a series of lines representing the overall mean and standard deviations (+/– 1, 2 and 3 sigmas).

The control chart data show the error reduction team's goal of 50% reduction was surpassed. Audits revealed the percentage of order entry errors consistently improved by 90% to less than 0.04 errors per bed every month for four months after the process changes.

POWER OF INFORMATION

Nurses now ask the team, "Why did we do all that extra work?" when referring to the former medication order entry process. The new process is simpler, works on all units and is more accurate. But the power of information is what will keep the staff from digressing back to old habits.

When audits showed an increase in transcription errors during the third week after implementation of the initiative, Alton Memorial knew exactly what to do. The reaction plan devised by the team was put into place, a root cause analysis was done, the source of error was removed and the process went back in control in no time.

As an Alton Memorial administrator said: "Finding out we had a problem even before we knew it and knowing exactly what to do to fix it was priceless."

References

1. Medication Errors and Patient Safety, www.ahrq.gov/qual/errorsix.htm.
2. National Coordinating Council for Medication Error Reporting and Prevention, www.mccmerp.org.
3. Pugh matrix, www.isixsigma.com/dictionary/glossary.asp.

Bibliography

1. BMG University, "Transactional Design for Six Sigma Course Manual," BMG, 2004, sections two and seven, www.bmgu.com.
2. Crow, Kenneth, "Performing QFD Step by Step," www.npd-solutions.com/qfdcons.html, 2005.
3. Evans, James, and William Lindsay, *The Management and Control of Quality,* sixth edition, 2005, pp 568–578.
4. Mazur, Glenn, Jeff Gibson and Bruce Harries, "QFD Applications in Health Care and Quality of Worklife," First International Symposium on

Quality Function Deployment, Union of Japanese Scientists and Engineers, Tokyo, March 1995.

5. Yang, Kai, and Basem El-Haik, *Design for Six Sigma: A Roadmap for Product Development,* McGraw Hill, 2003, pp: 49–68 and 173–196.

Yanira Benitez is business process leader and Six Sigma Black Belt for BJC HealthCare in St. Louis. She earned a master's degree in industrial engineering from Pennsylvania State University and is pursuing a doctorate at the University of Missouri. Benitez is a member of ASQ.

Leslie Forrester is a registered nurse and clinical information specialist/ educator for Alton Memorial Hospital, Alton, Illinois. She has a bachelor's degree in nursing from McKendree College, Lebanon, Illinois.

Carolyn Hurst is a registered nurse and medication safety officer for Alton Memorial Hospital. She has an associate's degree in nursing from Lewis & Clark Community College, Godfrey, Illinois.

Debra Turpin is a registered nurse and lead clinical information specialist at Alton Memorial Hospital. She has a bachelor's degree from McKendree College.

Faster Turnaround Time

Angelo Pellicone and Maude Martocci

IN 50 WORDS OR LESS

- After seeing an increase in patient volume, North Shore University Hospital implemented Six Sigma to reduce worsening delays in bed turnaround time.

- In six months, the Six Sigma team decreased its mean turnaround time by 136 minutes and went from 1 sigma to 2.3 sigma.

North Shore University Hospital (NSUH) in Manhasset, New York, is part of the North Shore–Long Island Jewish Health System in Great Neck, New York. In 2004, NSUH used Six Sigma to reduce noticeable delays in bed assignment turnaround time.

The hospital decided to concentrate on patient flow because it had started seeing increased patient volume, especially in the aging population, which made it difficult to balance capacity needs. Delays in the post anesthesia care unit (PACU) and the emergency department (ED) resulted in diversion (a situation in which the facility does not have the staff or available beds to accept additional patients), start time delays in the operating room (OR) and decreased patient and physician satisfaction.

After conducting a capstone project (see "Capstone Projects and Six Sigma," page 98) that focused on patient flow, the hospital realized staff were incorrectly using the bed tracking system (BTS)—an electronic system that describes the status of each bed. Delays in bed turnaround time resulted in delayed notification to the admission registered nurse—an RN who is responsible for the admission process—of a clean and ready bed. This often led to delays in OR throughputs and ED holds, and impacted the movement of patients throughout the hospital. The findings of this capstone project led to the Six Sigma project.

Reprinted with permission from Angelo Pellicone and Maude Martocci, "Faster Turnaround Time," *Quality Progress* (March 2006): 31–36.

CAPSTONE PROJECTS AND SIX SIGMA

North Shore–Long Island Jewish Health System, the third largest nonsectarian health system in the United States, is comprised of 14 hospitals. The system is currently in its sixth wave of Six Sigma training, having completed more than 60 projects. The system's Six Sigma institute is part of its corporate university, known as the Center for Learning and Innovation.

Since the program began, the center has trained 24 Black Belts, 70 Green Belts and two Master Black Belts. In conjunction with Six Sigma training, employees acquire valuable change management skills by taking classes in change acceleration process (CAP) and fast-track decision making.

CAP is a philosophy and tool set designed to help overcome cultural barriers to change by creating a shared need, shaping a vision and mobilizing commitment.

Fast-track decision making is North Shore University Hospital's version of General Electric's work-out process. It is a rapid problem-solving approach that includes team involvement and in-meeting decisions. This catalyst for change focuses on the process to drive improvement and empowers the people closest to the process to develop and implement appropriate solutions.

The health system also challenges employees with capstone projects that are designed to:

- Analyze the potential value fixing deficiencies will produce and compare it to the costs entailed.

- Isolate the two largest improvement opportunities and identify the fixed and variable associated costs. These costs cannot interfere with clinical quality.

- Make use of tools learned during CAP and the fast-track decision making session.

For additional information on North Shore–Long Island Jewish Health System, visit www.northshorelij.com.

The total turnaround time (TAT) in question extended from the time discharge instructions were given to the patient to the time the admission RN was made aware of a clean and ready bed. Many people were involved in the process of discharging a patient and preparing the bed for the next admitted patient. Communication among departments and staff members within each department was critical to ensure the patient flow process resulted in an efficient and timely experience.

HISTORY AND PROBLEM IDENTIFICATION

The project initially focused on one surgical nursing unit—the fourth floor Cohen Pavilion, or Four Cohen. Although it was a neuroscience unit, Four Cohen received patients from various entry points, including the PACU, ED and critical care. In 2004, Four Cohen had 2578 discharged patients.

Many hospital employees knew the TAT process was slow, but it was never measured to determine how slow. Once the Six Sigma team took a closer look at the process, it realized several factors were at play:

- Historically, the clerical support associate (CSA) was supposed to control the process but, according to policy, was not responsible for the process. Over time, however, the CSA ended up driving the process by default.

- The environmental services department's responsibilities within the process were monitored and constantly measured using the BTS. The perception throughout the hospital was that the response and TAT of environmental services was a major cause of the delay. In truth, this portion of the process—the time from when the discharged patient left the room to the time the room was clean— took an average of 55 minutes, which was better than the national standard.

- Although RNs were recognized as the patient care team leaders, communication among the team members and RNs was deficient. The patient care team consisted of an RN, a patient care associate (PCA), a support care associate (SCA) and a CSA. At the end of the process, admission RNs used three methods to determine if a clean bed was available: unit rounds; admission, discharge, transfer census; and phone calls from the unit. It was an inefficient, laborious process.

DEFINE AND MEASURE

During the define phase, the team developed a high-level process map (see Figure 1) that began when the RN gave discharge instructions to the patient and ended when the admission RN was notified of a clean and ready bed. After determining the primary customers were the admission RNs, the team surveyed them to establish the target and upper specification limits. This voice of the customer helped establish a target TAT of 120 minutes,

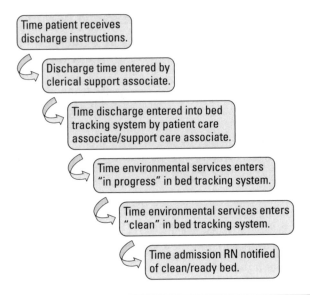

Time patient receives discharge instructions.

Discharge time entered by clerical support associate.

Time discharge entered into bed tracking system by patient care associate/support care associate.

Time environmental services enters "in progress" in bed tracking system.

Time environmental services enters "clean" in bed tracking system.

Time admission RN notified of clean/ready bed.

Figure 1 High-level process map.

with an upper specification limit of 150 minutes. A unit clock was used to ensure valid time measurement, and a data collection log sheet was created to measure the time between each step in the process.

The Six Sigma team conducted a fast-track decision-making session and used change acceleration process (CAP) tools, such as the threat/opportunity matrix, to establish buy-in from the Four Cohen staff to further justify the need for process improvement. The team explained that, if successful, the new process would present an even patient flow, which would lead to greater staff and patient satisfaction. If unsuccessful, there would be further delays in the ED and PACU and increased physician and patient dissatisfaction—all of which could lead to loss of revenue.

The team also permanently removed the CSA from the process because it needed to capture the true time the patient exited the room. The practice on Four Cohen, as in the rest of the hospital, was to have the CSA enter information into the BTS, even though the policy clearly dictated this was the responsibility of the PCA or SCA who escorted the patient from the room. Following the fast-track decision-making session, the entire staff was reeducated.

In the measure phase, the team first identified the data to be continuous. Then, it established operational definitions. A defect was defined as any time the TAT took more than 150 minutes. The team performed a measurement system analysis by having a team member on the unit shadow the process for one week. This measurement system proved 96.5% effective.

After collecting data on 195 patients, the team calculated the defects per million opportunities

$$\frac{\text{(Defects) } 130}{\underset{1}{\text{(Opportunities)}} \times \underset{195}{\text{(Total units)}}} \times 1,000,000 = 672,725 \text{ DPMO}$$

(DPMO):

The calculated DPMO of 672,725 equaled a score of 1 sigma. The mean, or average, TAT of the current process was 226 minutes, with a standard deviation of 170 minutes. After reviewing the data, the team set a goal to shift the mean to 120 minutes and reduce variation by 50%, to 85 minutes.

The team also completed a cause-and-effect diagram (see Figure 2) to help identify all the variables that impacted the TAT process. This tool helped target the vital X variables and gave the team direction as it began the analyze phase.

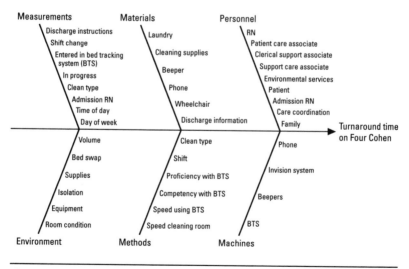

Figure 2 Cause-and-effect diagram.

ANALYZE AND IMPROVE

During the analyze phase, the variables that impacted the process (X's) were discussed and targeted for statistical analysis. The team sorted the data and distinguished between patients who were transferred to rehabilitation and those who were discharged home. For this particular project, the team decided to focus on the discharged patients because they were more within the hospital's control. The team then used a control impact matrix to prioritize the X's, highlight what was within the hospital's control and determine what had the biggest impact (see Figure 3).

The goal was to shift the mean TAT and reduce the standard deviation. Hypothesis testing involved searching for statistically significant differences in shift, day of week and length of time needed to complete each step of the process.

A graphical breakdown using an analysis of variance and a two-sample t-test proved there was no statistically significant difference in the process based on the day of the week or shift. Therefore, the team focused on the length of time needed to complete each step of the process. The null hypothesis said there was no difference in the amount of time needed to complete each step. It was rejected. The p-value = 0.000, which was less than 0.05; thus, the team concluded there was a statistically significant difference (see Figure 4).

As the team investigated further, it discovered both a communication and a technical failure at two key steps in the process that caused great delay.

			Impact		
		High	**Medium**	**Low**
Control	**In our control**	• RN discharge instruction. • Patient care associate/ support care associate. • Environmental services (ES). • Bed tracking system (BTS) process. • BTS proficiency. • Admission RN notified. • Condition of room.	• Care coordination. • Break time. • Beepers. • Cleaning supplies. • Shift change. • Specialty bed.	• Invision. • Clerical support associate. • ES travel time. • Scripts. • Wheelchair. • Phone.
	Out of our control	• Family. • Transport company/ emergency medical services. • Patient volume. • Isolation.	• Room change request. • Day of week. • Time of day. • Male vs. female.	• Patient. • Roommate.

Figure 3 Control impact matrix.

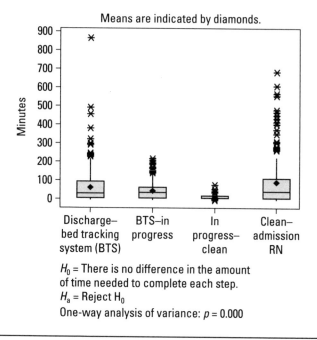

Figure 4 Turnaround time by each step in process.

An "ah-ha" moment arose when the team realized the staff lacked proficiency in using the BTS. This led to delays in the "time environmental services enters 'in progress' in BTS" step in the process. It was wrongly assumed the entire staff was adept. The lack of communication between the RNs and other patient care team members was then identified as a priority because it started the process. The lack of communication of a clean and ready bed to the admission RN was also identified because it was a more considerable cause of delay than originally expected.

Another ah-ha moment came when the team realized how efficient the environmental services part of the process was. It was not the problem!

FAST-TRACK DECISION-MAKING SESSION

Data were presented to the extended team and improvement strategies were discussed at a fast-track decision-making session. The staff came up with the following solutions:

1. Revise the discharge assessment sticker to include documentation of communication between an RN and a PCA/SCA.

2. Reeducate PCAs/SCAs on the use of the BTS. This training is now part of the orientation of all new patient care services staff and part of an annual mandated topics competency evaluation.

3. Create bedside laminated cards with BTS instructions.

4. Reformat admission RNs' beepers to the BTS to provide immediate notification of a clean and ready bed.

Once the project was turned over to its process owner, Four Cohen's nursing management team, the process went from a mean TAT of 226 minutes with a standard deviation of 170 minutes to a mean TAT of 90 minutes with a standard deviation of 71 minutes. The sigma score went from 1 sigma to 2.3 sigma at the end of the six-month project (see Figure 5).

A monthly individual and moving range chart was used to continue monitoring the TAT on Four Cohen (see Figure 6), and the improvements continued. Since the completion of the project, the TAT has improved to 69 minutes (see Figure 7).

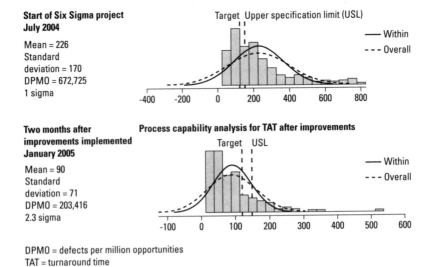

Figure 5 Change over time.

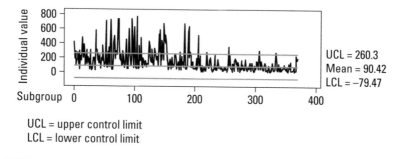

UCL = upper control limit
LCL = lower control limit

Figure 6   Individual and moving range chart.

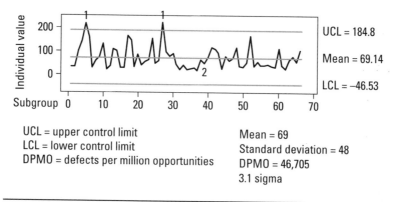

UCL = upper control limit
LCL = lower control limit
DPMO = defects per million opportunities

Mean = 69
Standard deviation = 48
DPMO = 46,705
3.1 sigma

Figure 7   Control chart for Four Cohen as of June 10, 2005.

ACTION PLAN

The success of the project and the response from the staff was so favorable, Four Cohen served as a pilot for the rest of the hospital. As a result of this project, and with the new emphasis on patient flow, there have now been rounds on all nursing units that include RNs, physicians and other members of the patient care team.

Patient satisfaction survey scores improved in two categories relating to discharge during the four months after the project ended. The first category—extent to which the patient felt ready for discharge—improved from 78.8 to 79.2. The second category—speed of discharge process—improved from 75 to 83.2.

Continuing with the success of this project, the hospital decided to conduct another Six Sigma project to address the time between the admission

RN being notified of a patient admission from the ED to the time the bed is assigned.

These initiatives have allowed the North Shore–Long Island Jewish Health System to view the admission and discharge process in a continuum. The efficiency of the admission process has a direct relationship to the efficiency of the discharge process. Although this was known qualitatively, the team was finally able to quantify it with data and metrics.

Angelo Pellicone is a Six Sigma Black Belt at the North Shore–Long Island Jewish Health System's Center for Learning and Innovation in Lake Success, New York. He earned a master's degree in healthcare administration from C.W. Post Long Island University in Brookville, New York.

Maude Martocci is the director of care coordination at North Shore University Hospital in Manhasset, New York. She earned a master's degree in healthcare administration from Hofstra University in Hempstead, New York.

Lean Six Sigma Reduces Medication Errors

Grace Esimai

IN 50 WORDS OR LESS

- Medication errors pose a serious threat in healthcare.

- A midsized hospital used Lean Six Sigma to change policy and practices to reduce these errors.

- After solutions were implemented, errors dropped sharply, labor costs fell, patients were more satisfied and employee morale improved.

Among healthcare errors, medication errors, including those made in prescriptions, pharmacy dispensing, handling by staff and handling by the patient in self-medicating situations, pose the most serious threat.

Interested in quality management in several areas, management at a midsized hospital (which chooses to be anonymous) approved a project using Lean Six Sigma to determine what changes in policy and practices might be necessary to significantly reduce these errors.

PROJECT TEAM

The group tasked with making this determination was set up in two tiers: a project team overseen by a steering committee.

The steering committee consisted of members of upper management and heads of functional Departments. This committee appointed employees with relevant daily floor-level experience in various associated processes as

Reprinted with permission from Grace Esimai, "Lean Six Sigma Reduces Medication Errors," *Quality Progress* (April 2005): 51–57.

members of the project team. Specifically, these individuals were involved in the processes of prescription transcription, order filling and all other steps influencing the error rate in the medication administration records (MARs).

In addition, the project team included individuals who could recommend and implement interventions to error reduction. The project team periodically reported to the steering committee.

DEFINING THE PROBLEM

The process of medication administration at a hospital involves six steps:

1. Selecting and procuring.

2. Storing.

3. Ordering and transcribing.

4. Preparing and dispensing.

5. Administering the medication.

6. Monitoring medication effects.

Due to time constraints, the steering committee defined the most urgent problem as the unknown error rate in the hospital MAR. The scope of the project was to concentrate on the medication order entry (OE) process. The project team charter aimed to investigate a process to dramatically reduce MAR errors by a factor of about 1000 by the end of the project's five-month duration.

MEASURING THE BASELINE AND TRACKING ERRORS

Prior to the formation of this project team, the hospital's quality improvement department had mapped the pharmacy OE and the nursing MAR transcription processes. The project team reviewed and verified the process maps against the current practices and sequence of operations.

The team reviewed the errors observed in February in the pharmacy OE process. An effort was then made to more rigorously define these errors and establish the criteria for cataloging them to aid in root cause analysis and achieve better consistency in error tabulation. This attempt minimized subjectivity and thus achieved a more consistent result overall. The project team subsequently identified the following errors:

- *Additional instructions:* Any physician comments/instructions/indications on the original faxed medication order that are not input by pharmacy.

- *Dose:* Wrong dose or dose differs from original faxed medication order.

- *Drug:* Wrong drug (medication description differs from original faxed medication order).

- *Duplicate order entry:* Same medication description profiled twice with two different prescription numbers.

- *Frequency:* Frequency on MAR differs from original faxed medication order.

- *Omissions*: Certain medication is omitted from the OE process without a reason.

- *Discontinuation order not carried out when received:* Medication that is either indicated or implied to be discontinued may still be entered in the OE by pharmacy.

- *Order not received:* Faxed medication order is not received or can not be located at the pharmacy.

- *Patient:* Medication order has been profiled correctly/incorrectly on the wrong patient.

- *Route:* Medication order has been profiled with incorrect route (intravenous or intramuscular).

The Pareto diagram of the data gathered at the start of the project is shown in Figure 1. The diagram prioritizes the relative frequency of occurrence in a bar chart for better visualization. At project initiation, the total error rate in the overall MAR process was estimated to be 0.33% or about 3300 per million.

While reviewing weekly records, the team observed certain errors could be traced back to the pharmacy employee who committed them. The team quickly tabulated the errors and discovered a high variability in performance among these employees.

Some employees committed as many as 112 errors in the two-month period of February and March, while others made as few as zero errors in that same period. There were 21 employees involved with the OE process. Figure 2 shows the results.

To protect their identities, the project team coded the employees using a simple number scheme. For immediate intervention, the team reviewed

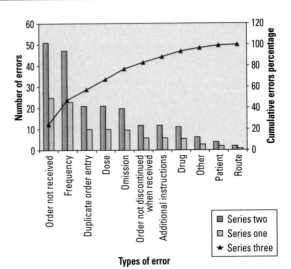

Figure 1 Pharmacy error Pareto diagram.

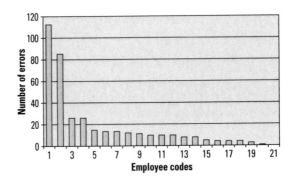

Figure 2 February and March errors by pharmacy employees.

the errors during one-on-one meetings with the pharmacy employees and found the high error frequencies resulted from a misunderstanding of certain guidelines and instructions. To correct this, the pharmacy department instituted remedial education and closer supervision of employees.

The next step was to estimate the trend of the errors vs. time. Statistical methods for estimating the trend included moving averages, exponential smoothing and least squares or regression analysis. On running a regression

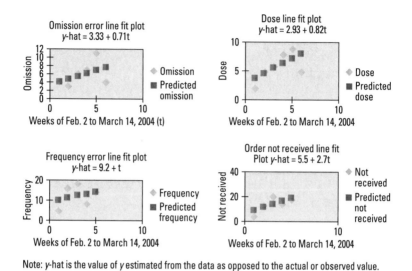

Note: *y*-hat is the value of *y* estimated from the data as opposed to the actual or observed value.

Figure 3   February and March errors showing positive trend.

analysis, our choice as the most objective method, evidence of increased errors became obvious (see Figure 3).

VITAL MISSING DATA AND METRICS

The basic metric of Six Sigma identifies defects per million opportunities, which can also be represented as a percentage error rate. Error rates are computed from the ratios of the total number of errors associated with a population of transactions and the total number of transactions in the population.

To establish a context for identifying the medication OE errors (or MAR errors) at the hospital, here is an outline of the process sequence: Daily orders are faxed to the pharmacy, where they are profiled on the MAR. Nurses review the MAR and report any error findings to the pharmacy. A pharmacy technician then records the errors by type and who committed them. In this arrangement, it is very difficult to capture errors, such as forgetting to fax an order, that are committed by the nurses themselves. The pharmacy is thus blamed for every error, and there is no accountability at the nurses' end for MAR errors.

Another pertinent and vital metric, albeit elusive, is the average order cycle time. This is defined as the average time it takes the pharmacy to fill an order measured from when a physician writes a prescription to when it registers on the MAR as correct.

This metric was not available because the physicians did not write the time of the prescription. They simply wrote the date. It would be important to have such information so root causes of delays could be studied and interventions implemented.

This implementation was especially necessary because it could contribute to labor cost savings as well as the satisfaction of the internal customers (nurses), the internal vendors or customers (pharmacists) and external customers (patients).

ANALYZING THE PROBLEM

Finally, after all the investigation, the project team found the root causes of all the different types of errors to be one or a combination of the following:

- There were problems with the fax machines that used regular telephone lines, and related technical problems caused unnecessary delays, duplicate order entries and nonreceipt of faxed orders in the pharmacy.

- Problems with the legibility of physicians' handwriting and use of personal nonconventional abbreviations were partly responsible for wrong doses, drugs and frequencies. Some drug errors arose from the use of generic vs. trade names.

- Distractions and interruptions during the order entry process, such as phone calls or questions and conversations with colleagues, caused omission errors, the selection of incorrect drugs or doses from the dictionary, wrong frequency and duplicate order entries.

- Nonreconciliation among nurses and pharmacists regarding the physician's orders regarding the standard way to administer the medication, such as the route, number of times a day and when during the day.

- Other common cause and human errors such as not discontinuing orders when received due to oversight, dispensing wrong doses due to becoming used to a certain dose and selecting medication from nursing station floor stock and forgetting to note a change in dose.

During the investigation, the project team also observed that the number of human errors could have arisen from stressful and dissatisfactory work conditions. The team therefore decided each of the two work groups involved should fill out a customer satisfaction survey on their perception of needs and expectations of the other group. Figures 4 and 5 give the nurses' survey results. Figures 6 and 7 display the results of the pharmacists' survey of the nurses.

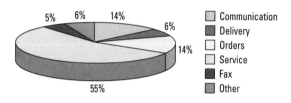

Figure 4   Nurses' satisfaction with pharmacy.

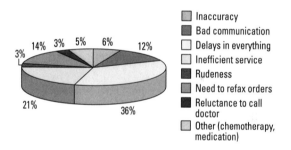

Figure 5   Things nurses disliked about pharmacy.

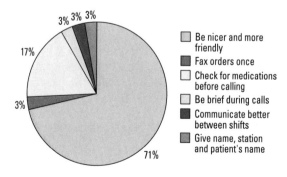

Figure 6   Pharmacists' satisfaction with nurses.

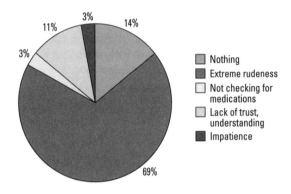

Figure 7 Things pharmacists disliked about nursing department.

It is interesting to note from Figure 5 only 3% of the nurses said the pharmacy employees were rude, contrasting with the overwhelming majority of pharmacists from Figure 7 who claimed the nurses were extremely rude (69%) and impatient (3%).

Apparently, the nurses at this hospital were not friendly and polite to the pharmacists as they carried out their daily duties. They seemed to fail to recognize they and the pharmacists were customers of each other, deserving the same courtesy they offer their external customers, the patients. Each group believed the other group expected them to do the impossible, understanding neither the nature of its work nor its workload.

DEVELOPING ERROR-REDUCING SOLUTIONS

The project team combined lean methods and Six Sigma techniques in the error reduction process. Lean methods generally aim at the identification and gradual evolutionary elimination of waste (error).

The Six Sigma techniques use statistical procedures and five well-defined phases of the define, measure, analyze, improve and control (DMAIC) roadmap to achieve profitability and quantum gains in quality, sometimes as a result of redesign of the process maps and installation of new equipment.

In healthcare, the best approach appears to be error prevention using software that flags mistakes so employees will take immediate corrective action. The project team therefore approved or recommended the following solutions:

- *Institution of a high performance standard through instruction and supervision.* The project team discovered factors contributing to substandard performance and increasing the error trend, including the misunderstanding of instructions and guidelines by some pharmacists. A higher performance standard was immediately instituted through instruction and supervision. This effort, using lean methods, yielded significant positive results.

- *Facilitywide (full) implementation of computerized physician order management (CPOM).* The project team considered the CPOM program paramount to reducing or permanently eliminating errors caused by illegibility of physicians' handwriting and faxing of handwritten orders. Timelines would be monitored because the exact time a prescription was written would be recorded, thus eliminating undue delays.

- *Installation of a system to separate the fax and phone lines as an interim measure to reduce the faxing problems.* We believed this step would reduce the errors related to nonreceipt of faxed orders at the pharmacy and duplicate orders, reducing man-hours and tension between the nursing and pharmacy employees.

- *Unit-based pharmacists and agreement on standard times of medication administration among hospital nurses and pharmacists.* If the pharmacists were unit based, some understanding of each other's job and its scope would likely develop between pharmacists and the nurses in each unit. The work therefore would become streamlined, and nurses and pharmacists would know their internal customers by name— an added bonus to customer satisfaction.

- *Monthly meetings to foster better relationships between nurses and pharmacists.* This will help eliminate wrong perceptions nurses and pharmacists currently hold of each other's jobs and help change a stressful workplace to a place where people work cordially as a team to achieve the common strategic goal— patient care and satisfaction.

- *Designation of a pharmacy employee to serve as a telephone operator for all external calls.* During the analyze phase, the team found distractions from outside phone calls caused numerous errors. A solution could be designating a pharmacy employee to take these calls so the pharmacists can concentrate on what they are doing.

IMPLEMENTING AND SUSTAINING THE SOLUTIONS

Considering the available data from February to June, you can observe progress in the error reduction effort. The simple linear regression analysis of each of the errors clearly shows a downward trend (see Figure 8).

Figure 9 shows that most of the errors have been dramatically reduced, with the total number dropping from 213 in February to 96 in June, a 55% reduction. Figure 9 also clearly shows the differences in absolute numbers between the February and June frequencies for each type of error.

The team further made a comparison of February and June OE errors by pharmacist. Figure 10 shows a significant reduction for most of the

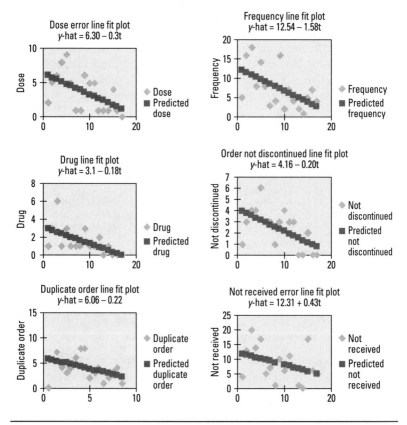

Figure 8 February to June weekly errors showing negative trend.

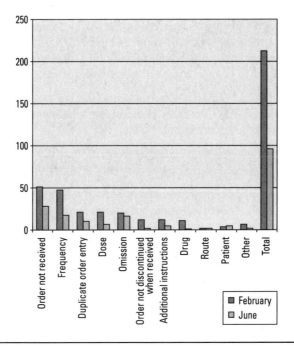

Figure 9 February and June pharmacy order entry errors by error type.

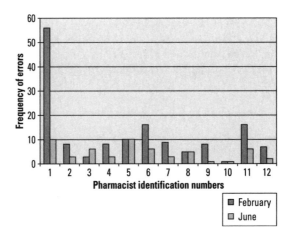

Figure 10 February and June errors by pharmacist.

pharmacists. The nonpharmacist errors caused by faxing problems and recorded as "orders not received" continued to be high, although an almost 50% reduction (from 51 in February to 28 in June) was attained.

Other benefits of instituting a Lean Six Sigma methodology at this midsized hospital were:

- Reversal of OE errors from an increasing to a downward trend for most types of errors.

- A decrease in the total error rate from 0.33% to 0.14% in five months.

- Estimated labor cost reductions of $550,000 (annualized at $1.32 million). It is noteworthy that the current results are realized by simply creating awareness through pharmacy department meetings and fresh instructions and training to the pharmacy employees.

- Patient satisfaction.

- Improved employee morale and better relationships between nurses and pharmacists.

Acknowledgments

The author thanks Ken Kipers, MD, Victor Eriken and Chimdimnma Esimai for their useful suggestions.

Bibliography

Barry, Robert, Amy C. Murcko, and Clifford E. Brubaker, *The Six Sigma Book for Healthcare,* Health Administration Press, 2002.

Ficalora, Joe, Joe Costello, and Julien Renaud, *Combining Lean and Six Sigma Methodologies,* special publication of the ASQ Statistics Division, Spring 2004.

Till, David W., *The Recipe for Simple Business Improvement,* ASQ Quality Press, 2004.

Grace O. Esimai is a senior lecturer in the department of information systems and operations management at the University of Texas at Arlington. She earned a doctorate in statistics at Iowa State University and is a member of ASQ.

Quality Intervenes at a Hospital

Jennifer Volland

IN 50 WORDS OR LESS

- The Nebraska Medical Center used quality methods in its interventional radiology department to turn around a decline in patient volume.

- The result was more patients and more satisfaction for patients, employees and referring physicians.

The Nebraska Medical Center is a 735-bed nonprofit hospital in Omaha. Made up of two merged facilities—Clarkson Hospital and the University of Nebraska Medical Center—it is the largest teaching hospital in the state, with both academic and private practice physicians. It began implementation of Six Sigma in December 2002, with this definition as a guide: Six Sigma is "a statistical measure of performance of a process or product; a goal that reaches near perfection for performance improvement; and a system of management to achieve lasting business leadership and world-class performance."[1]

The Nebraska Medical Center's interventional radiology department was selected as one of the first areas of focus through the hospital's project selection process. With a staff of 12 to 15 nurses, radiology technicians and physicians, this department performs a wide variety of invasive procedures, including placing urethral stents, transjugular liver biopsies, and procedures using fluoroscopy and chemoembolization.

In October 1997, physician loss and process inefficiencies were causing patient volume to decline. By 2002, it still hadn't improved, as dissatisfied referring physicians were sending patients to other hospitals. Patients who

Reprinted with permission from Jennifer Volland, "Quality Intervenes at a Hospital," *Quality Progress* (February 2005): 57–62.

remained were experiencing delays in their treatments, another problem. The interventional radiology department was well aware this was hurting the medical center's revenue and the satisfaction of patients and referring physicians.

DEFINING THE PROBLEM

A Six Sigma project team was assembled to address problems in the department's scheduling process (see Figure 1) and increase both the number of patients seen and the volume of procedures the department was conducting. Key project team members included the lead nurse scheduler, lead technologist and department manager.

The lead nurse scheduler speaks to the referring physicians and clinics to schedule patients for procedures. The lead technologist and other

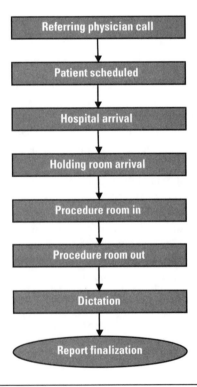

Figure 1 High-level process flow.

technologists are responsible for setting up the surgical area where procedures are done, running the equipment and assisting the interventional radiologist doing the procedure. The technologists know the supplies needed for each case and are able to pull whatever is needed for the physician while keeping everything sterile. The department manager is a former technologist.

Physician involvement was also initiated early in the process with ongoing input and information sharing from the two physicians on staff. Two additional physicians joined the department after the initiation of the project and were added as valuable resources to the team.

During the first phase of the define, measure, analyze, improve, control (DMAIC) cycle, it became clear scheduling was a primary concern for referring physicians. Physicians who referred a high volume of patients expressed difficulties their clinic staff had reaching the interventional radiology scheduler: the current process involved calling a pager first, phone calls were often placed on hold, and it sometimes took multiple attempts to set up an appointment time. Referring physicians wanted appointments scheduled in one call.

The referring physicians also had many patients who lived out of town, and once a patient left a clinic, it was often difficult to reach him or her. Setting an appointment time for the interventional radiology procedure would be much easier if it could be done while the patient was still in the office. With clinic nurses waiting for the nurse scheduler to return phone calls, it was clear easier communication was needed.

At the time, the nurse scheduler was also the lead nurse for the department, which often resulted in him or her being pulled from scheduling duties to help in the holding room, an area where the staff nurses perform pre-procedure tasks for the patients, such as starting intravenous peripheral lines, completing nursing assessments and giving medications. The duality of the role created stress in the position, and other nurses in the department were often frustrated when they needed to cover the scheduler's role. There were ample opportunities for improving processes and increasing job satisfaction.

Along with the referring physicians and nurses in the department, the interventional radiologists and technologists also experienced frustration with scheduling. Both groups said the scheduling information form was inadequate, with information slots on the form left blank or pertinent information missing. Often the nurse scheduler knew the information from the clinic interaction, but the information was not consistently written on the form because of time constraints and the belief that some items on the scheduling form were redundant or not necessary.

MEASURING THE CURRENT PROCESS

During the measure phase the project team members collected data on the scheduling process. They discovered it took an average of 1.4 calls to schedule an appointment. But the biggest problem was the amount of variability—it could take up to seven calls, with a standard deviation of 0.989. Additionally, scheduling an appointment took an average of 32.17 minutes, and at times up to 298 minutes, depending on the procedure (standard deviation of 59.36 minutes). There were often prior X-ray or treatment films to be reviewed or schedule time coordination needed with the computerized tomography (CT) department. It was clear too much time and effort were being spent on processes that could be streamlined.

CHANGES IN THE SCHEDULING PROCESS

In the analyze and improve phases, the project team and department staff started to identify changes that could be made for process improvement early on. To address scheduling concerns, a Work-Out was held with seven high-volume referring clinics, the interventional radiology nurse scheduler and the department manager to determine what they needed to streamline the scheduling process and make scheduling easier.

The Work-Out concept was originally developed at General Electric and consists of highly facilitated sessions.[2] There are three main steps:

1. A sponsor challenges key individuals who know a process best—people who actually use the process as part of their jobs—to solve a problem.

2. This team of process experts is allowed to create solutions while being led by a facilitator trained in specific change process dynamics and team facilitation tools. This facilitator is often called a change agent.

3. At the end of the Work-Out, the sponsor returns, examines the proposed solutions and renders a decision of yes, no or needs more information.

When done right, Work-Outs have the ability to rapidly drive decision making and change through an organization to overcome everyday problems and identify critical to quality (CTQ) needs. CTQ needs are expectations by customers based on what matters most to them.[3]

Assembling the Work-Out team was a valuable experience for all involved. People who had never worked together were able to meet and collaboratively address common problems. Silos that existed between the clinics and the interventional radiology department began to break down as concerns were discussed face-to-face.

From the Work-Out it was discovered that communication in scheduling with the department was not the only CTQ need. Clinics were uncertain which procedures were scheduled directly through the interventional radiology department and which procedures went through centralized scheduling for other radiology departments. A quick win determined early in the Work-Out was to make available a complete list of procedures that occurred in the interventional radiology department. Clinics could refer to this list to know which procedures were scheduled through the department and use it as a tool in training their new employees.

Another CTQ need in the scheduling process was to give clinics the ability to reach an actual person when they called for scheduling. The current process involved calling a department pager number, with the scheduler returning the page to the clinic. If the scheduling nurse was with a patient or in the holding room, it could be a while before the call was returned.

The number of calls to schedule was also identified as a concern by the clinics. The project team was not so much concerned about the average of 1.4 calls. With the maximum number of calls at seven, they were most concerned with reducing the variability in the process.

The clinics were also uncertain of what information would be requested when scheduling was done. Different information could be asked for depending on the individual scheduler. Clinics sought consistency and awareness of what information would be required when they called so they could readily provide it.

COLLABORATION LEADS TO IMPROVEMENT

The Work-Out spurred further discussions and team-building opportunities for the interventional radiologists, technologists, nurses and scheduler. They examined and redesigned the scheduling slip—more informational items were added—and agreed on how the form was to be consistently filled out. Copies of the revised form were sent to the high-volume referring clinics so they would know in advance the information that would be requested. The clear and complete scheduling slip also made things easier for the nurses who covered for the regular scheduler.

Another difficulty was scheduling CT scanner time, since this required additional coordination and calls. CT scans are needed for any patient undergoing a biopsy. The Nebraska Medical Center revisited this issue using its new change management methodologies. Based on the current volume of cases requiring CT scanner rooms, the CT department agreed to allocate two one-hour time slots per day exclusively to the interventional radiology department. This change reduced the number of calls necessary to schedule time in the CT department and guaranteed available time.

Further improvement was made by the interventional radiology physicians reaching consensus on time allocation for procedures and lab work needed prior to procedures. This allowed for continuity of lab work requested and the amount of procedure time allocated by the scheduler. The consistency helped the scheduler know what lab work to tell the clinics was needed independent of the interventional radiologist, who was often not assigned until the day of the procedure.

The interventional radiologists also agreed on approval types for needed procedures. Procedures could require either front-end approval (interventional radiologist approval needed before scheduling an appointment), no approval or a new category—back-end approval. With back-end approval interventional radiologists still needed to approve the case, but an appointment time could be given when the referring clinic called to schedule. This category was for cases that just required additional film review prior to patient arrival. These cases could be scheduled immediately and discussed the following day during the department physicians' morning meeting.

Since calling the pager was a concern for the clinics, the process was changed to calling a direct department phone number. If the scheduler was not at the desk, then the call was rerouted to the pager. This change streamlined the process and reduced the variability in how many calls were needed to schedule an appointment.

The responsibility of coordinating patients from the holding room into the procedure room, previously held by a nurse, was given to a tech, which allowed the nurse scheduler more time for scheduling. The tech understood the functionality of equipment in the procedure rooms and could give more attention to the job. This change ultimately decreased overall patient time spent in the holding room.

As another process improvement, the team developed patient information sheets and gave them to the high-volume referring clinics. These sheets outlined items that were important for the patient to know about their procedure, aiding communication between the patient and the department. On the back of the information sheets were maps illustrating the location of the interventional radiology department for the day of the procedure.

ACHIEVING SUCCESSFUL RESULTS

Although the average number of calls to schedule remained unchanged, the maximum number of calls was reduced from seven to three, with the standard deviation decreasing from 0.989 to 0.52 calls (Figure 2). The referring clinics felt the change, and the department recognized additional reduction in the average number of calls could be harmful to patients, as further collaboration between referring physicians and interventional radiologists was sometimes needed when scheduling more-complex cases.

Minutes to schedule increased from 32.17 to 33.18 on average. However, with the changes in the scheduling slip, better quality of information was obtained at the time the clinics were calling to schedule, which reduced the need for calling back for additional information. The extra minute allowed for exchange of all necessary information during the first call, reducing the need for subsequent calls back to the department.

With all the changes implemented (Table 1 and Figure 3), complaints from the referring clinics were reduced to zero. One clinic staff member noted, "It's much easier to reach the scheduler, and calls are returned sooner." Similar comments were made by high-volume referring physicians to the department. One said, "After the Six Sigma project, scheduling for procedures is going much better. I don't have problems now."

By using Six Sigma tools, the department was able to collaborate with referring clinics and its own staff on improving its scheduling process. Many of the changes not only improved efficiencies, but also strengthened relationships between the department and referring clinics.

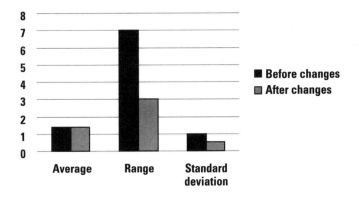

Figure 2 Interventional radiology calls to schedule.

Table 1   Interventional radiology changes.

Lean

Scheduling slip reexamined and redesigned to capture pertinent information.

Agreement on how to fill out the scheduling slip.

Reduction in calls to schedule through obtaining block time from the computerized tomography department.

Interventional radiologists agree on allotted procedure times.

Interventional radiologists agree on lab work to be done for procedures.

Interventional radiologists agree on approval type needed for procedures.

Six Sigma

Room coordination role changed from a nurse to a radiology technician.

Patient information sheets designed with maps on the back.

Work-Out

Clinics received a list of procedures done in interventional radiology.

Ability to call in to a person rather than dialing a pager.

Clinics received copies of scheduling information needed.

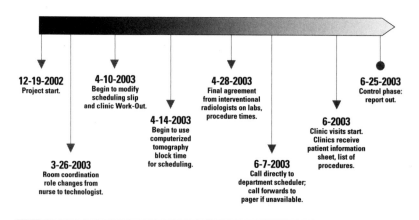

Figure 3   Project timeline.

The Work-Out between the external clinics and department staff allowed individuals to meet face-to-face and begin to build relationships through better communication of what each needed to perform his or her job well.

Job satisfaction was improved by making the position of the scheduler easier, establishing clear expectations of which lab procedures would be required and standardizing approval type and amount of time a procedure needed to be scheduled. Not being pulled to different job functions created a win for both the nurse scheduler and the clinics impacted by the process.

Most importantly, in the fiscal year 2003–04, the interventional radiology department saw 4649 patients, a more than 21% increase over the 3829 patients served in the previous fiscal year that reflects improvements in patient and referring physician satisfaction and process efficiencies.

References

1. Pete Pande and Larry Holpp, *What Is Six Sigma?* McGraw-Hill, 2002.
2. Ron Snee and Roger Hoerl, *Leading Six Sigma: A Step-by-Step Guide Based on Experience with GE and Other Six Sigma Companies,* Prentice Hall, 2003.
3. Greg Brue, *Six Sigma for Managers,* McGraw-Hill, 2002.

Acknowledgments

The author gratefully acknowledges from the Nebraska Medical Center: Glenn Fosdick, CEO; Steve Smith, chief medical officer; Sue Korth, outcomes and performance improvement director; the interventional radiologists; department staff; project team; Terry Paulsen, project sponsor; Pat Fryant, department manager; and high-volume referring clinics for their dedication to Six Sigma and substantial improvements made through their collaboration. Recognition is also given to GE Medical Systems, specifically Phil Kaczmarski, David Green and Carolyn Pexton, for their support and mentoring of the Six Sigma process.

Jennifer Volland was a Six Sigma Master Black Belt at the Nebraska Medical Center. She received her nursing degree from Creighton University in Omaha. She also received an executive MBA from the University of Nebraska in Omaha where she is currently working toward her doctorate in public administration with an emphasis in healthcare administration and policy.

Toward Error-Free Lab Work

Project Leads to $339,000 in Added Revenue and Cost Reduction for Hospital Lab

Nancy B. Riebling, Susan Condon, and Daniel Gopen,
North Shore–Long Island Jewish Health System

In a clinical laboratory, reliability can not be achieved through the control of accuracy in the analytical phase of the testing process alone because studies have shown 70 to 85% of laboratory errors occur before that—in the preanalytical phase.[1]

Analytic standards are set by established quality control criteria, but no such standards exist for defining the quality of the preanalytical phase—an important component of total laboratory quality consisting of specimen procurement, accessioning and transport.

Accessioning is a registration process. It occurs when the information in the paper requisition that accompanies a sample is entered into the lab information system, and a label is generated and placed on the sample tube.

North Shore–Long Island Jewish (LIJ) Health System, headquartered in Great Neck, New York, launched a Six Sigma project last year to reduce the number of accessioning errors at its core laboratory, which performs more than 3.5 million tests annually.

Created in 1998, North Shore LIJ's laboratory model consists of a strategically located core laboratory using total laboratory automation, a rapid response laboratory in each of the system's 18 hospitals, a standardized laboratory information system, standardized laboratory instrumentation and consolidated testing at the core laboratory.

Work for the core lab comes from hospitals, long-term care facilities, clinical trials, physician offices and reference testing (complex tests). The lab performs approximately 65% of the routine testing for the North Shore

Reprinted with permission from Nancy B. Riebling, Susan Condon, and Daniel Gopen, "Toward Error-Free Lab Work," *Six Sigma Forum Magazine* 4, no. 1: 23–29.

LIJ network as well as all the network's microbiology, special tests, molecular diagnostics and reference testing.

As part of the laboratory's ongoing performance improvement process, accessioning errors had been measured historically for years. It was a chronic problem for which consultants had previously been engaged without arriving at a successful resolution.

At the core lab, a multidisciplinary team of technical, compliance, marketing, quality and accessioning management staff was assembled to tackle its first Six Sigma project using the define, measure, analyze, improve, control (DMAIC) approach.

The accessioning project aligned with the core laboratory's strategic plan of increasing market share in the region and becoming number one among its competitors on measures of customer satisfaction. The lab's customers include patients, hospitals, private physician offices and private nursing homes.

DEFINING AND MEASURING
THE PROCESS

During the define phase, the team developed a high-level process map (see Figure 1) beginning with the initial step of the physician's filling out the

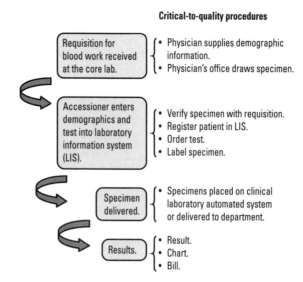

Figure 1 High-level process map.

requisition and drawing the specimen and ending, when the result and chart for lab work is produced for the patient.

After conducting a survey to obtain the voice of the customer from physician practices, the Six Sigma team developed an ICD-9 Common Diagnosis Codes Pocket Guide to help physicians supply the correct diagnosis code for each laboratory test. ICD-9 codes are one of the required fields on a laboratory requisition.

Through careful data collection and analysis, the team found that 5% of the specimens accessioned at the core lab were inaccurate or incomplete. This defect rate was in line with historical data. These inaccuracies cause delays in reimbursement and decreased customer satisfaction.

The Six Sigma team then used change acceleration process tools, such as the threat/opportunity matrix, during the define phase to obtain buy-in from the laboratory staff for the necessity of pursuing this project.

If successful, the lab would be able to increase productivity and customer satisfaction while decreasing the number of incomplete or inaccurate

BUSINESS RESULTS

North Shore–Long Island Jewish Health System, headquartered in Great Neck, New York, is the third largest nonsectarian health system in the country, comprising 18 hospitals.

The system is currently in its fifth wave of Six Sigma training, having completed more than 40 projects. The Six Sigma institute is part of the health system's corporate university, known as the Center for Learning and Innovation.

Since the program began, the Center for Learning has trained 24 Black Belts, 70 Green Belts and three Master Black Belts. In conjunction with Six Sigma training, employees acquire valuable change management skills by taking classes in change acceleration process and fast-track decision making.

Change acceleration process is a philosophy and tool set designed to help overcome cultural barriers to change by creating a shared need, shaping a vision and mobilizing commitment. Fast-track decision making (North Shore's version of General Electric's Work-Out process) is a rapid problem-solving approach with team involvement and in-meeting decisions.

It is a catalyst for change focusing on the process to drive improvement and empowering the people closest to the process to develop and implement appropriate solutions.

For additional information on the system, go to www.northshore-lij.com.

requisitions. If unsuccessful in the long term, the core lab's reputation would be diminished, leading to a loss of revenue.

In the measure phase, the first order of business was to determine the operational definitions. The team defined a defect as a laboratory requisition with missing or inaccurate demographic, test or ICD-9 information.

The team performed a measurement system analysis by giving the requisition-checking staff a test of 25 requisitions—some good, some bad. The gold standard was the accessioning manager, who knew which were good and which were defective. Each requisition was rated as good or bad depending on whether all seven fields were entered in the laboratory information system correctly. If any field was incorrect, the requisition was considered defective.

The team gave the test to the staff on two separate occasions. The gauge R&R study demonstrated repeatability, reproducibility and accuracy were more than 90% in all cases. A review of 5607 laboratory requisitions collected over a one-week period revealed a defect rate of 283.

There are seven opportunities for defects in each requisition (name, Social Security number, date of birth, gender, physician, test and ICD-9 code):

$$\text{Defects per million opportunities (DPMO)} =$$
$$\frac{D}{(U)(O)} = \frac{283}{(5607)(7)} = 7210$$

The calculated DPMO of 7210 was a 3.9 sigma score.

The team also measured staff productivity by calculating the average number of requisitions processed per hour as 17, with a standard deviation of seven requisitions per hour.

The team completed stakeholder analysis to aid in determining a strategy to move those individuals who were moderately against the project to a more supportive position. It also helped identify those individuals who were likely to touch the process and thus could be a resource to the team.

ANALYZING AND IMPROVING PROCEDURES

In the analyze phase, the team benchmarked the core laboratory's performance against other reference laboratories throughout the country.

The core laboratory is a certified member of the College of American Pathologists. This certification entails peer review inspections of the facility and quality benchmarking study participation to compare the performance of laboratories throughout the country.

The sponsor of this project and chairman of the department of laboratories for the health system aided the team by putting it in contact with other large reference laboratories on the West Coast.

The core lab's accessioning error rate of 3.9 sigma was comparable to industry standards. The productivity of the accessioning staff showed that the current process had a large variation in the number of requisitions processed per hour and was below industry standards.

The goal was to decrease our DPMO by 50% as well as increase staff productivity to the industry standard of 20 requisitions per hour with a decrease in variation to two requisitions per hour.

Graphical analysis using Pareto charts (see Figure 2) indicated 50% of the accessioning errors were due to incorrect entering of the Social Security number for skilled nursing facility patients. This discovery was an enlightening observation, or "ah ha"! Before the analysis, the team members had been convinced the culprit would be the handwriting of physicians when they fill out the name on the requisition.

This "X" proved statistically significant utilizing the chi-square test. The null hypothesis that all types of demographic errors are the same was rejected because the p-value = 0.002 was less than 0.05, and thus the team could conclude a statistical difference in the number of defects existed among the different demographic fields.

As the team drilled down utilizing the five whys tool,[2] it found that the skilled nursing facility used addressographs for patient demographic information. Addressographs have multiple identifiers, making interpretation difficult for the accessioning staff.

In addition, addressographs tend to be illegible when run through an addressograph machine. Peel-off bar code labels located on the bottom of the core lab's patient charts (which already existed) could be placed on the laboratory requisition and scanned in accessioning for the pertinent demographic information, thus eliminating the need for addressographs with multiple patient identifiers on laboratory requisitions (see Figure 3).

Each accessioning bench was already equipped with a bar code wand that could be used for scanning the codes. Graphical analysis using Pareto charts determined a small percentage of the staff (five out of 24 full-time employees) was making the majority of the errors. This again proved to be statistically significant with the chi-square test.

After the team's review of the data to determine cause and effect for why a small percentage of staff was making the majority of errors, a new training program for staff was developed in the improve phase.

The team also created desktop reference guides to be positioned at each accessioning station. This helped make all the information new hires were supplied with at orientation and training readily available. The manual

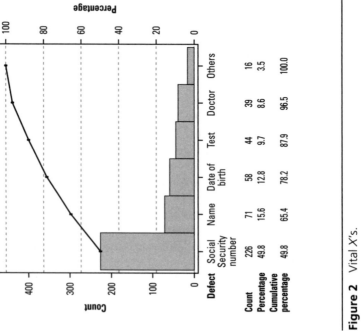

Figure 2   Vital *X*'s.

Addressograph

Doe John
MR 0102195
359B ORIG-AD
12/09/1999
DOB 08/08/1921
MCARE084121422
MCAID DE008471P
HIP084121422

Bar code label

• Competency checks for staff.
• Desktop reference guide.
• New hire checklist.

Figure 3   Improvement strategy for patient demographics.

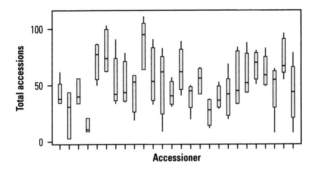

Figure 4   Box plots of total accessions by accessioner.

was broken into user-friendly tabs using the voice of the customer from the accessioning staff.

Ongoing competency assessment was achieved by using blind proficiency specimens throughout accessioning. The team modeled the assessment on the proficiency testing programs performed in the technical areas of the laboratory that are required for licensing. Box plots of accessioner (those who do the labeling of specimens) productivity showed that the core lab lacked established best practices. Through analysis, the team concluded it was the process—not the people—driving the error rate for accessioning (see Figure 4).

FAST-TRACK SESSION

Specimen movement within the lab was a "heartburn issue" for lab staff. To address the problems, a fast-track decision-making (FTD) session was held. The issue presented to the frontline supervisors and employees of the accessioning and technical departments was how to facilitate the movement of specimens from the nontechnical to technical area of the lab.

The session led participants to propose three recommendations:

1. A runner position—someone to move specimens around the accessioning department.

2. A color-coded book that lists all lab tests and which department performed the analysis.

3. Color-coded signs throughout the lab matching the color coding in the book so accessioning staff knows where to deliver specific specimens in the laboratory.

The empowered staff implemented recommendations two and three within the 90-day FTD time frame. The employees designed the signs and books. The project was a huge success and generated buy-in for the Six Sigma team's improvement strategies.

The response from the employees was so favorable the idea was translated to other key areas within the laboratory, such as marketing and information services.

Using lean and Six Sigma principles, the team was able to streamline specimen movement within the accessioning department, resulting in increased capacity (see Figure 5). Instead of each accessioner retrieving his or her work from the receiving sample bins and then delivering work to the clinical laboratory automated system, a lead accessioner position was developed. This role was given to an experienced person who would deliver 20 requisitions per hour to each accessioner, pick up completed work, place it on the robotics and answer technical accessioning questions when making rounds.

The Six Sigma team performed design of experiments (DOE) to determine whether the use of bar codes on the laboratory requisitions, distribution of specimens and expertise of the accessioning staff had any effect on the number of accessioning errors and the productivity of the staff per hour.

Through a full-factorial design of three factors each at two different levels using analysis of variance, main effects and interaction plots, the team was able to show that the use of bar codes and distribution of specimens was

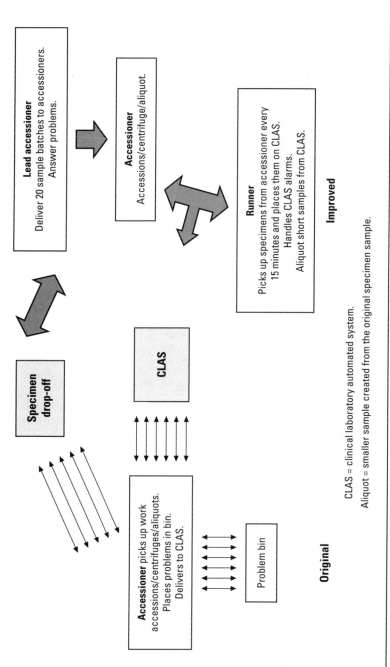

Figure 5 Specimen movement.

statistically significant (see Figure 6). The *p*-value of 0.047 also demonstrated that the variation was not caused by random chance.

The team developed an elevator speech that was presented to the accessioning, the marketing staff and outreach clients to stress the importance of using the bar codes provided on the patient's charts for patient demographics on laboratory requisitions.

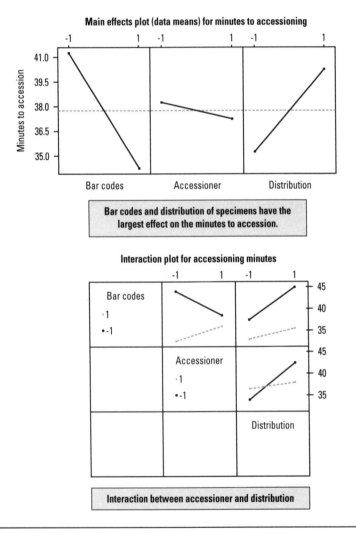

Figure 6 Analyzing the factorial design.

The DOE helped demonstrate to the staff that the new lean workflow helped increase productivity and the bar codes reduced accessioning errors.

CONTROLLING RESULTS

In the control phase, the Six Sigma team implemented a plan that incorporated individual and moving range charts for monitoring accessioner productivity.[3] The DPMO for accessioning errors is now monitored on a monthly basis. The Six Sigma metric has become part of the laboratory quality management program. Blind proficiency testing is performed on a monthly basis and is also incorporated into the laboratories' quality monitors.

At the end of the control phase, the process went from a 3.9 sigma to a 4.2 sigma. The accessioning department was able to increase its capacity and handle the 43% increase in outreach specimen volume that occurred in the first quarter of 2003 without additional full-time employees. The improvements from this project resulted in a combined financial impact of $339,000 a year due to increased revenue and cost reduction.

The Six Sigma team turned the project over to its process owner in May 2003 and disbanded. Currently, the productivity of the accessioning staff is more than 23 requisitions per hour, with a standard deviation of two requisitions per hour. The DPMO for accessioning errors is 1387 with a 4.5 sigma level (see Figure 7). The proficiency score for the accessioning staff is 99%.

Six Sigma, lean and change management gave the team the tools it needed to fix the process and sustain the improvements.

References and Notes

1. Bonini Pierangelo, "Errors in Laboratory Medicine," *Clinical Chemistry,* Vol. 48, 2002, pp. 691–698.
2. For definition of the five whys tool, go to www.asq.org/sixsigma/terms/index. html.
3. For more information on individual and moving range charts, see *How to Use Control Charts for Healthcare* by D. Lynn Kelly (ASQ Quality Press, 1999).

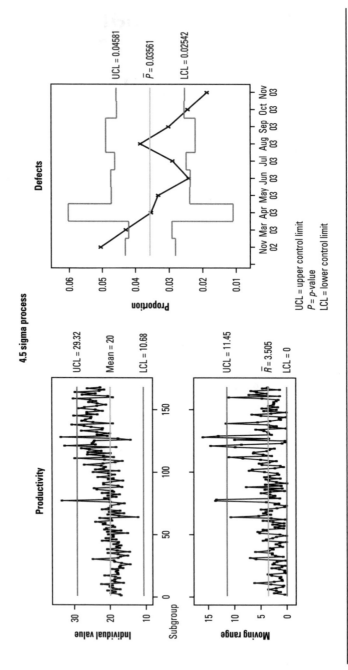

Figure 7   Control.

Healthcare Department Reduces Cycle Time and Errors

Project Adds Revenue of About $202 per Patient

Donna Powers and Mary Paul, North Shore–Long Island
Jewish Health System

In early 2005, North Shore–Long Island Jewish Health System in New York identified key financial opportunities related to improving revenue cycle, charge capture and coding. These issues would form the basis for the system's next wave of Six Sigma projects.

The patient financial services department then identified an opportunity for improvement in the department of ambulatory chemotherapy and transfusion (ACT), which provides chemotherapy infusions, chemotherapy-related injections and blood transfusions for 20,000 outpatient visits per year.

The department asked that a Six Sigma team address operational workflow processes at the Long Island–Jewish campus because it estimated the department lost between $250,000 and $500,000 (net) in 2004 as a result of uncoded charts and missing charges.

Administration believed that inefficiencies and complexities in the billing process adversely affected the ability of patient financial services to submit accurate bills in a timely manner. In fact, there was no assurance the system was getting paid for services rendered.

The health system would soon be opening a new, state-of-the-art facility. If the processes weren't fixed in the old location, they were not going to be the best they could be in the new building.

Reprinted with permission from Donna Powers and Mary Paul, "Healthcare Department Reduces Cycle Time and Errors," *Six Sigma Forum Magazine* 7, no. 2: 30–34.

BACKGROUND AND TERMINOLOGY

Revenue cycle refers to the set of processes that manage the business components of a case and are in place from preadmission through discharge to ensure the highest likelihood of timely reimbursement.

Charge capture refers to the set of processes and controls to ensure that all services provided during the life of a case are recorded in the billing system and that charges for those services are appropriately set.

Coding refers to the set of processes and controls in place to ensure that what is done for the patient is properly interpreted. Different services provided to the patient are then combined on a record and communicated using several industry coding systems for purposes of risk adjustment, severity of illness and billing/reimbursement.

Our team included an experienced Black Belt with a background in clinical nursing, administration and operations, and Green Belts from finance, information systems, oncology nursing and oncology billing. Functionally and hierarchically, we had the right members on the team.

Patient satisfaction scores in the ACT were the medical center's highest, and we met early resistance merely suggesting that anything change. But, looking at a high-level process of an ACT visit from registration to the time the bill was generated and sent out opened everyone's eyes to the excessive number of handoffs, absence of a consistent operational workflow process and amount of rework being done.

The team capitalized on reducing the amount of rework necessary to correct defects, allowing clinical staff to have more face time with patients. If the project was successful, then we could increase revenue and provide opportunity for growth while improving quality of care and staff morale. We addressed operational performance and quality, both of which were in alignment with the health system's strategic plan.

PROJECT SCOPING

The project was scoped to include missing drugs, procedures, transfusions and visits. The Six Sigma team determined that what were critical to quality were the number of bills going out with errors (big Y) and the lag time associated with charge entry and the uniform bill (UB) being sent. UB is the standard to which all hospitals conform so every hospital has the same format for billing.

The team broke down the process into several steps or buckets:

- Patient registers with correct account number and insurance pre-authorization for the procedure; patient demographic information sheet generated.

- Registered nurse (RN) administers treatment, documents the injection on a shot list, sends the orders to pharmacy and records charges on a "super bill."

- Pharmacist enters drug charges into the pharmacy system.

- Coder reviews chart, transfers diagnosis and procedure charge codes to face sheet and attaches super bill.

- Charges entered into the health information system.

- A super coder (final pass) randomly checks bills before they go out.

- Billing completed (UB sent to insurer).

COLLECTING THE DATA

Data collection during the measure phase involved looking at defects in all of the fields necessary to bill accurately and calculating how long it took to enter charges and complete the billing.

For the discrete data, we were defective 58% of the time. That meant that one or more fields necessary to complete an accurate bill were missing or incorrect. Continuous data showed that the department had excessive cycle time. Cycle time from date of service (DOS) to charge entry was 3.7 days, and DOS to billing was 13.6 days. It took almost two weeks to send a bill that was accurate 42% of the time.

The ACT process had a first- and final-pass yield built into its existing process. The first pass was done by the coder in the ACT unit. We found that the coder spent excessive time reconciling missing information.

Diagnosis and physician documentation, including history and physical, accounted for 94% of what was missing the first time through. The coder had to track down and hound the physicians for information before the bill could be sent on to have charges entered.

The final pass was done by a second medical records coder, who randomly selected and checked bills for accuracy and returned them to ACT for error correction. Once the coder obtained the information, first pass showed records were correct 97% of the time, and final yield showed records were correct 93% of the time. That didn't make sense.

We found that diagnoses present when the original coder reviewed the chart were missing when the second coder reviewed them (see Figure 1). We suspected there was a software interface problem because only three of a possible five diagnoses made it from the health information system to the uniform bill.

During analysis of our discrete data, we found that pharmacy charges were a vital X. Two-thirds of errors were related to a highly manual process

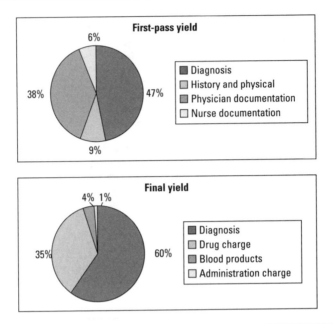

Figure 1 What coders were missing.

of capturing and entering charges, and the lack of a mistake-proof inventory control process (see Figure 2).

Pharmacists, who were dispensing and mixing highly toxic chemotherapeutic agents, were spending considerable time entering drugs into a log book and then entering the charges into a computerized pharmacy system. Nurses could take very expensive drugs out of an unlocked cabinet without advance documentation.

For continuous cycle time, the inputs that made a difference were day of the week and volume of patients. High variability by day and volume was probably due to lack of scheduling for injection patients (see Figure 3). ACT historically had never scheduled its injection patients—they simply showed up on the day and at the time they wished to be treated. What might have been an acceptable practice when ACT was treating 10 patients a day had turned into chaos when treating 70.

Chronically ill patients had been coming for weekly treatments for years. The staff was extremely concerned that requiring them to make appointments and adhere to a schedule would affect ACT's high patient satisfaction scores. Because the nurses were very resistant to any change that would result in reduced patient satisfaction, the team had to be respectful of this when it came to improvement.

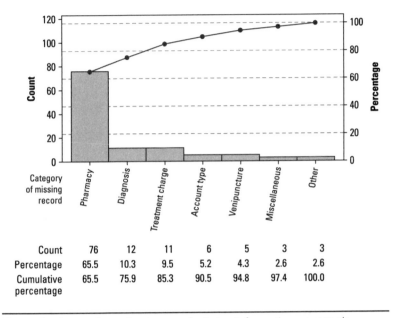

	Pharmacy	Diagnosis	Treatment charge	Account type	Venipuncture	Miscellaneous	Other
Count	76	12	11	6	5	3	3
Percentage	65.5	10.3	9.5	5.2	4.3	2.6	2.6
Cumulative percentage	65.5	75.9	85.3	90.5	94.8	97.4	100.0

Figure 2 Pareto chart of category of missing information on records.

Before beginning the improvement phase, we addressed the software interface issue. Information systems validated that the fourth and fifth diagnoses were not being transferred from one system to another due to an interface disconnect. Staff promptly fixed the problem.

Although missing authorization was not significant during analysis, one case was found that represented $76,000 in unbilled charges. Lack of preauthorization was slipping through the cracks.

ON TO IMPROVEMENT

The improvement phase dealt specifically with each vital X we had identified. To address the issue of missing pharmacy charges, the team used a combination of an automated medication dispensing system and a manual inventory control process.

The department had previously purchased an automated dispensing system console, which was not in use due to incorrect charge entry to the ACT accounts and the fact that there was hospitalwide access to the accounts. Once the team solved the issue through a major education initiative, drugs were loaded into the system, and staff was trained.

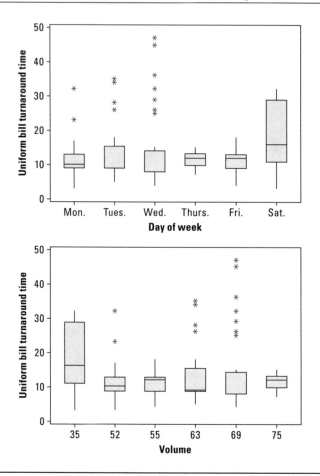

Figure 3 Box plots of cycle time for bills.

We ran a pilot program with a relatively inexpensive and low-volume drug category. After a successful trial, subsequent drug categories were added by cost and volume to ensure we had a mistake-proof process in place.

We were unable to place four medications into the automated system because Medicaid required they be billed at the lowest possible billing unit. This would require customized computer pharmacy billing to calculate the appropriate billing units. The hospital was not willing to invest in that at the time.

Unfortunately, two of the four drugs were high-cost items. To deal with this obstacle, the team developed a manual inventory control system. The injections were placed into a locked box, injection documentation lists were reformatted so the lines matched the amounts given out and the pharmacy would replenish the supply only if all usage lines were filled in and all injections accounted for.

When all medications are in the automated system, we will have totally eliminated two of the manual steps in our high-level process map (see Figure 4).

Cycle time was related to several variables. First, there was the issue of implementing scheduled appointments while ensuring the patient experience would be positive. Posters and flyers initially introduced the patients to the change. Each patient received an individualized explanation of the reasons for and potential benefits of the change. The explanations concentrated on reduced wait times and more efficient service. We scheduled the patients' next appointments at that time to make the transition easier.

As long as ACT was going to begin scheduling all patients, the team decided to introduce computerized scheduling, which was a bonus. A letter apprised physicians of the changes to scheduled appointments and computerized scheduling.

Coders were spending excessive time reconciling missing information. We reformulated the super bill or charge ticket so it was simple for RNs to complete and easy for coders to read.

Order sets for the shot or injection patients were not standardized and were confusing for the medical staff in terms of which International Code of Diseases (called ICD9) to select. ACT revised the order sets with input from the medical staff and the coders, making it possible to provide consistently accurate information the first time. We had a laminated pocket card

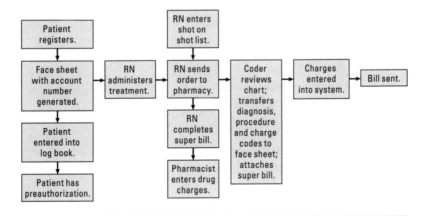

Figure 4 High-level process map.

created for the medical staff to provide guidance as to which code to select for the most common diagnoses.

The unit receptionists in the ACT were easily distracted while entering charges because they were also answering phones, scheduling patients and dealing with families at the same time.

In addition, they were short by 2.4 positions, which represented 50% of their actual full-time equivalents. ACT set up a quiet, separate environment for the unit receptionists to enter charges four hours per day and gave the receptionists a goal and expectation of 15–20 charges entered per hour. Once they were allowed to do their work without interruption, their output improved dramatically.

We dealt with missing authorization by holding a fast-track decision-making session, cleaning up the process of insurance verification and putting a process into place for obtaining referrals.

IMPRESSIVE IMPROVEMENT

The progress made three months after the improvements was impressive, and the customers clearly perceived a difference. The billing error defect rate decreased by 72%, with an increase in sigma score from 1.5 to 2.6 (see Table 1).

The lag time for date of service to charge entry decreased from 3.7 to 2.4 days, with an increase in sigma score from 1.3 to 2.1. Date of service to bill being sent decreased from 13.6 to 5.9 days, with an increase in sigma score from .6 to 1.5. (see Tables 2 and 3).

The process owner monitored progress for the next year and continues to tweak the process. As this article was being prepared for publication, the following improvements had been made:

- Defect rate was at an all time low of 2.5% from an initial metric of 50% defective.

- Cycle time from date of service to charge entry met the goal because the improvements were implemented.

- Cycle time for sending bills hovered at or near the goal.

- Missing diagnoses were virtually eliminated (see Table 4).

- The medical center recovered $68,000 of lost revenue on one patient who was missing authorization.

- The automated medication dispensing system eliminated clerical work for nursing and pharmacy staff, resulting in significantly

Table 1 Big Y billing errors.

	Before Six Sigma	After Six Sigma	December '05	January '06	February '06	January '07
Defect rate	50%	15%	10%	13%	14%	2.5%
DPMO	496,000	158,000	96,000	133,000	142,857	25,000
Sigma	1.5	2.5	2.8	2.6	2.6	3.4

Table 2 Sub y date of service to charge entry.

	Before Six Sigma	After Six Sigma	December '05	January '06	February '06	January '07
USL (days)	3	3	3	3	3	3
Mean (days)	3.7	2.7	3.1	2.24	2.4	2.4
SD (days)	3.1	1.4	1.5	0.52	0.44	1.49
DPMO	584,845	418,702	527,340	289,077	288,057	350,000
Sigma score	1.3	1.7	1.5	2.0	2.1	1.9

Table 3 Sub y date of service to bill sent.

	Before Six Sigma	After Six Sigma	December '05	January '06	February '06	January '07
USL (days)	6	6	6	6	6	6
Mean (days)	13.6	8.8	7.8	7	5.9	6.8
SD (days)	8.5	2.9	5.1	3.6	1.7	4.2
DPMO	813,590	834,068	644,209	576,517	488,161	554,912
Sigma score	0.6	0.5	1.1	1.3	1.5	1.4

DPMO = defects per million opportunities, USL = upper specification limit, SD = standard deviation

Table 4 Missing diagnoses.

Month	Total uniform bills	Missing diagnoses	Percentage
April	879	169	19%
May	1641	207	13%
June	1437	51	3%
July	1284	31	2%
September	701	13	2%

improved employee satisfaction and morale. Nurses and pharmacists are no longer manually entering charges for all but four drugs.

- Although the staff was quite concerned about scheduling injections, patients raised almost no issues. The transition from no scheduling to computerized scheduling was completed, and patients adjusted well. Staff ensures that appointment times are honored and that patients are treated in a timely manner.

- The unit has maintained its excellent patient satisfaction scores. Patient financial services was so pleased with the results that the department eliminated the random check of bills before they go out, and medical records recovered half of a full-time employee.

Based on this trial data, missing charges per patient has been reduced by $202, which results in nearly $4 million in potential revenue annually.

Standardizing Healthcare Projects

Generic Templates Are Useful for Early DMAIC Phases

Ronald J. M. M. Does, Thijs M. B. Vermaat, Henk de Koning,
and Søren Bisgaard, University of Amsterdam, and
Jaap van den Heuvel, Canisius Wilhelmina Hospital

The project-oriented deployment of teams to solve specific well-defined chronic problems is core to Six Sigma. Indeed, this capitalizes on J. M. Juran's wise observation that "quality problems are solved project by project and in no other way."[1]

It is well known that poor project definitions and early-stage planning are two of the common causes for project failure. The project definition, captured in the project charter, specifies the deliverables, among other things. The deliverables indicate the quantifiable benefits expected to result from completing the project.

But expected deliverables are often vague and poorly stated. As a result, it is not uncommon that the project developers, Black Belt (BB) and Green Belt (GB) project leaders and project owners (Champions) have diverging views of what constitutes a successful project. Wasted effort, missed deadlines and even conflicts might result.

HEALTHCARE PROJECT CATEGORIES

By studying how several Six Sigma projects in healthcare unfolded in practice (see "Hospital Implementation Examples," p. 152) and reconstructing the underlying structure of the projects, we found about 90% of the healthcare related Six Sigma projects in our sample fell naturally into six generic project categories:

1. Increasing the number of admissions.

2. Increasing the efficiency of processes.

Reprinted with permission from Ronald J. M. M. Does, Thijs M. B. Vermaat, Henk de Koning, and Søren Bisgaard, "Standardizing Healthcare Projects," *Six Sigma Forum Magazine* 6, no. 1: 14–23.

3. Reducing poor use of materials.

4. Reducing deficiencies.

5. Improving the planning and scheduling of human resources.

6. Improving the utilization of facilities and equipment.

Clearly our sample does not qualify as a scientific survey, but it does indicate a pattern. Note we have used a grounded theory approach to develop these categories.[2, 3]

Each generic project category is characterized by particular define and measure phases.[4] Those can typically be captured succinctly by a high-level process description, a critical-to-quality (CTQ) flowdown and operational definitions of the selected internal CTQs.

Thus, by reviewing a large number of Six Sigma projects from healthcare, we have tentatively developed a few generic templates for executing the different generic project categories—an example of the Pareto principle at work.

This set of standard templates for project definitions can facilitate the formulation of specific project deliverables for each of the six generic project categories.

A clear project definition with explicitly stated goals greatly increases the odds of successful project completion, especially for novice Six Sigma

---

HOSPITAL IMPLEMENTATION EXAMPLES

Commonwealth Health Corp., with the help of consultants from General Electric Co., was one of the first healthcare organizations to implement Six Sigma. Commonwealth has about 500 beds and is a multisite health system with its headquarters in Bowling Green, Kentucky.

In the United States, several healthcare organizations have followed the Commonwealth example. They include the Charleston Area Medical Center, a 919-bed three-campus hospital in West Virginia; the Thibodaux Regional Medical Center, a nonprofit 149-bed hospital in Louisiana; and Mount Carmel Health System, a three-hospital system in Columbus, Ohio.

In Europe, the Institute for Business and Industrial Statistics at the University of Amsterdam, the Netherlands, has spearheaded the implementation of Six Sigma in several hospitals in the Netherlands and Belgium.

Examples include the 384-bed Red Cross Hospital in Beverwijk, Netherlands; the 635-bed Canisius Wilhelmina Hospital in Nijmegen, Netherlands; and the 567-bed Virga Jesse Hospital in Hasselt, Belgium.

teams. The templates must be seen as preliminary and a good starting point for further research. Indeed, the format given for the templates could be expanded to more general Six Sigma projects.

Projects at hospitals we worked with in the Netherlands and Belgium constitute the majority of our sample and illustrate the generic project types.

In each hospital, the implementation of Six Sigma started with a one-day introductory orientation and training for upper management and directors. This training was followed with more-detailed training of about 15 GBs in the Six Sigma methodology, typically lasting eight days over a five-month period.

To stimulate commitment to Six Sigma, participants initially could choose their own projects. As the number of projects increased, the need to coordinate and manage the Six Sigma program more closely became evident as we observed GBs having difficulty completing their projects.

A Master Black Belt (MBB) was appointed to start a project management control system to evaluate progress and support GBs in finishing their projects. The MBB organized the necessary training programs and facilitated the process of assigning follow-up projects to teams after the previous project was completed.

As Six Sigma was rolled out through each organization, other coworkers would typically show interest in attending GB training. GB training programs began for new groups of about 15 employees every six months. Participants emerged from different departments and disciplines within the organization.

We also developed a special training program for medical specialists and started training employees from partner organizations. For example, personnel from home care and nursing homes were also interested in initiating projects. These projects typically improved interorganizational cooperation, communication and ultimately the quality of care.

DEFINING HEALTHCARE PROJECTS

Six Sigma projects are managed rigorously according to the define, measure, analyze, improve and control (DMAIC) strategy. Each phase is completed only when specific milestones are reached. At any given time it is possible to assess a specific project's status in a standardized way within departments and across the entire organization, much like the stage-gate approach.[5]

In the define phase, projects are selected. The project selection process results in a definition of the project's objectives. Project definitions are often started with different levels of specificity, precision and complete-ness. Goals might be tangible and specific, for example, in terms of metrics or performance indicators. Most goals are not. Typically they lack an opera-tional form, and deliverables are ambiguous.

The measure stage is devoted to clarification of the objectives of the project in terms of measurable and quantifiable indicators. The objective of this step is to translate the more or less specific project definition into one or more measurable indicators. In Six Sigma terminology such measurable indicators are called CTQs.[6]

A commonly used tool to go from a project definition to CTQs is the CTQ flowdown.[7] This tool makes the rationale underlying the project explicit by showing hierarchically how CTQs relate to higher-level concepts such as performance indicators and strategic focal points.

Viewed downward, the CTQ flowdown shows how CTQs relate to spe-cific measurements. This is done by providing so-called operational defi-nitions.[8] They help make CTQs measurable by specifying a measurement procedure.

Choosing a measurement procedure means, among other things, speci-fying the unit or sample to be used. If you measure weekly complaint num-bers, the unit is a week. If you measure throughput time per file, the unit is a file. If you measure length of stay of patients in a hospital, the unit is a patient.

By providing operational definitions for CTQs, a template for data col-lection—a measurement plan—is defined. A measurement plan has the structure of a data matrix. The rows of the data matrix correspond to units. For each unit there is a CTQ value and thus a row in the data matrix or data set. The columns of the matrix correspond to CTQs.

While we believe our sample of 100 projects is reasonably represen-tative of the kind of projects encountered in practice, different categories might be found in other cultural environments, BB vs. GB projects, training backgrounds or countries.

As indicated in Figure 1, projects that aim to increase efficiency account for 37% of the projects; to reduce deficiencies, 28%; to increase admissions, 11%; and to reduce use of materials, 7%.

Cumulatively, these four types account for more than 80% of all proj-ects we have encountered. Only 4% of the projects in our sample were a combination of two or more generic types.

Finally, about 5% of the projects did not belong to any of the generic categories. Indeed, some of these projects were related to marketing or investment decisions. We believe this is yet another manifestation of the Pareto principle.

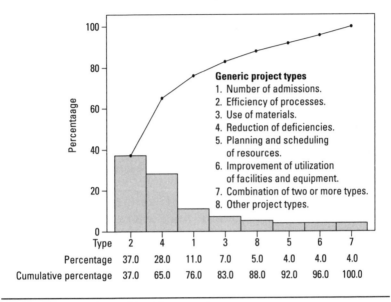

Figure 1 Pareto chart of healthcare projects.

Note there is some overlap between projects to increase the number of admissions and those to increase the efficiency of processes. We have split these two categories because the former deals with extra revenues, and the latter focuses on reducing costs.

Furthermore, there is overlap between projects to improve the planning and scheduling of resources and those to improve the use of facilities and equipment. The reason to split these two categories is that the former deals with personnel and the latter with facilities and equipment.

CATEGORY 1.
INCREASING ADMISSIONS

Hospitals and other healthcare institutions earn money by admitting and curing patients. The Dutch hospital funding system pays fixed prices for admissions, first contacts and day-care treatments.

Recently, the Dutch government gradually began to introduce a new billing system based on so-called diagnosis treatment combinations, which is similar to the diagnosis related groups system that also is used in the United States.

Both systems are applied simultaneously at this time and greatly resemble a capitation system. The consequences of both systems are that treating more patients provides more income, but delivering more or higher-quality care or providing better service does not provide more income. Hence, a key revenue driver is the number of patients admitted in a given time interval. Admissions can be increased by shortening the length of stay under the assumption that there are enough patients.

Figure 2 shows this relationship. Key performance indicators and internal CTQs should be measured in the corresponding process. To relate the length of stay and bed occupation to specific measurements, operational definitions are needed (see Figure 3).

A typical way to reduce the length of stay is to conduct a value stream analysis of the clinical pathway of a given disease or medical condition. A value stream analysis often uncovers redundancies in activities, examinations and administration, which can result in unnecessary time that adds little or no value for the patient or the healthcare institution.

Other non-value-added activities that waste time were caused by:

• Waiting for the results of diagnostic measurements.

• Waiting due to capacity problems in operating rooms.

• Waiting because of shortage of diagnostic scanners.

• Waiting because of shortage of home-care facilities.

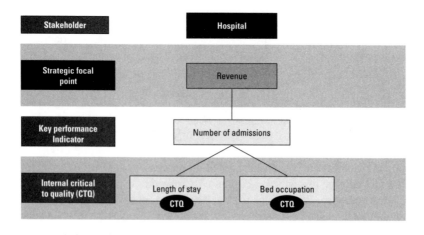

Figure 2 CTQ flowdown for projects aimed at increasing the number of admissions.

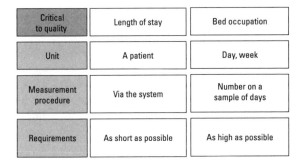

Critical to quality	Length of stay	Bed occupation
Unit	A patient	Day, week
Measurement procedure	Via the system	Number on a sample of days
Requirements	As short as possible	As high as possible

Figure 3 Operational definitions for projects aimed at increasing the number of admissions.

Example: Consider a project aimed at reducing the length of stay of chronic obstructive pulmonary disease (COPD) patients at one hospital. The internal CTQ was length of stay. Bed occupation was considered only as a secondary metric, and it should not change for the worse.

Patients were admitted to either the pulmonary or internal medicine department because of capacity problems in the former. Analysis showed the average stay in the pulmonary department was two days shorter than in the internal medicine department. A statistical analysis showed this difference was not due to patient characteristics or physicians. Apparently the pulmonary department was just better at treating pulmonary patients.

Thus, the hospital administration went for the obvious solution: the bed capacity was rebalanced so all COPD patients were admitted to the pulmonary department. After this change, inpatient days were reduced, and more admissions were possible. The annual benefits were estimated to be $40,000 per year.

CATEGORY 2.
INCREASING PROCESS EFFICIENCY

Projects that aim to increase efficiency of processes constitute the second cluster. Whether it is a patient seeking care or an external party requesting information, efficiency is often measured in terms of throughput time—the time from the service request to the time the service is fully delivered. Throughput time can be broken down further into waiting time, processing time and the amount of rework necessary if certain steps have to be redone.

To measure hospital efficiency you need to compute the number of productive hours and the number of items produced. Figure 4 shows the four internal CTQs of a typical efficiency improvement project. The CTQs can be put into operational form, as indicated in Figure 5.

Example: An efficiency project was aimed at improving the use of operating rooms at one hospital. The Six Sigma team immediately focused on starting on time in the morning and using all available time. The official start time was 8 a.m. Data collected in the measure phase showed the average start time was 8:33 a.m.

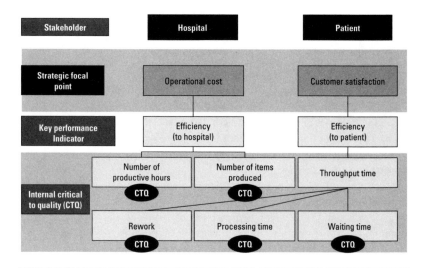

Figure 4   CTQ flowdown for projects aimed at increasing efficiency.

Critical to quality	Processing time/ waiting time	Rework	Number of productive hours/ number of items produced
Unit	Patient (or request/file)	Patient (or request/file)	Day/week
Measurement procedure	Via measurement form	Via measurement form	Via the system
Requirements	As short as possible	Zero	As high as possible

Figure 5   Operational definitions for projects aimed at increasing efficiency.

While 33 minutes might not sound like a lot of time, for this hospital with eight operating rooms and an average of 250 days in a year, it added up to 1100 lost hours or 137.5 full days each year that could have been used for productive work. Furthermore, operating rooms in a modern hospital are very capital-intensive units with highly skilled and thus highly paid staff. Such waste and inefficiency could not be tolerated.

During the analyze phase, the GB team identified several causes for starting late, including:

- Patients brought in late.

- Patients not having been given proper medication.

- Insufficient nursing staff.

- Surgeons late.

- Anesthesiologists late.

After more in-depth analysis, the GB team discovered that the underlying cause was a poorly defined planning process. They designed a new admission process based on a few simple rules: patients must be in the operating rooms no later than 7:35 a.m., data must be collected to ensure patients have received preoperative medication before arriving at the operating theater, and the referring department and anesthesiologist have to be informed one day in advance of a scheduled procedure.

To control this new planning process, visual management was introduced. This system showed the start times for each operation in a given operating room during the past week. The resulting graph was reviewed weekly during a regularly scheduled staff meeting. This project yielded an annual savings of $273,000.

Example: Most hospitals have facilities for preparing intravenous medication, traditionally done in the nursing departments. At one hospital, a project was started to reduce the preparation time. The Six Sigma team measured processing time and rework per patient. Transferring preparation activities from the nursing departments to the pharmacy, and using a new procedure for injections resulted in estimated annual savings of $42,500.

CATEGORY 3.
REDUCING POOR USE OF MATERIALS

Use of materials is another driver of operational cost. Total cost of materials is driven by volume—or number of units—used and cost per unit. In projects in which the objective is to improve material use and lower costs, volume and cost per unit are typically selected as internal CTQs (see Figure 6). The operational definitions of volume and cost of usage are shown in Figure 7.

Example: A hospital found that some patients on expensive intravenous antibiotics could have been switched earlier to much less expensive oral medication. A standard operating procedure (SOP) for switching from intravenous to oral medication was then developed. Strictly following this SOP resulted in an estimated annual savings of $75,000. In this case, only one of the two CTQs, volume of usage, was improved. The other, the unit cost, was not considered.

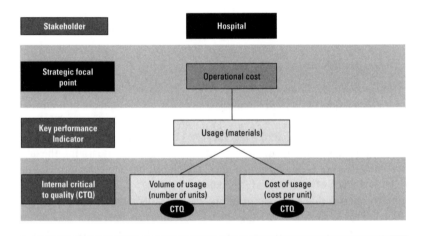

Figure 6 CQT flowdown for projects aimed at reducing material usage.

Critical to quality	Volume of usage	Cost of usage
Unit	Day	Day
Measurement procedure	Via the registration system	Via the registration system
Requirements	As low as possible	As low as possible

Figure 7 Operational definitions for projects aimed at reducing material usage.

CATEGORY 4.
REDUCING DEFICIENCIES

Healthcare deficiencies include defects, infections, complaints and no-shows. Reducing deficiencies generally will drive costs down. In some cases—for example, reducing complaints—the effort to eliminate deficiencies mainly will increase customer satisfaction. Thus, we suggest two generic strategic focal points for this problem category (see Figure 8). The CTQs can be volume and time or cost. Figure 9 shows their operational definitions.

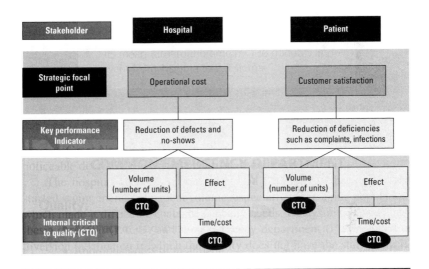

Figure 8   CTQ flowdown for projects aimed at reducing deficiencies.

Critical to quality	Volume (number of units)	Cost or time
Unit	Day	Complaints/infections/no-show
Measurement procedure	Via the registration system	Via the registration system
Requirements	Zero	As low as possible

Figure 9   Operational definitions for projects aimed at reducing deficiencies.

Example: The Red Cross Hospital in the Netherlands issues about 250,000 invoices yearly to patients and insurance companies. Of these, an average of 9% are refused and returned due to the hospital's mistakes.

After an in-depth study of the process by a GB team, problems were identified and process improvements were implemented. At the time of this writing, less than 1% of the invoices were being refused. This translated into savings exceeding $200,000 per year.

CATEGORY 5.
IMPROVING RESOURCE
PLANNING AND SCHEDULING

The planning and scheduling of resources, specifically human resources, is another major category. Quite often, departments and teams are inappropriately staffed because of poor planning. This is particularly alarming given that 60 to 70% of a hospital's annual budget consists of costs related to personnel.

Projects in which planning and scheduling of resources are improved usually consist of two internal CTQs:

- The amount of human resources needed.

- The amount of human resources actually used.

The project's CTQ is typically the difference between resources needed and those actually used. The objective should be to reduce this difference as much as possible. Figure 10 shows how this CTQ relates to operational cost. Operational definitions can be seen in Figure 11.

Example: In general, the required number of nursing staff during a shift depends on the bed occupation. Based on a time series analysis of the varying occupancy rate, it is possible to forecast the required number of staff needed. This required number then can be compared with the number of nursing staff actually used.

In the pediatric department of one hospital, a Six Sigma team conducted a retrospective study and found that the staff dramatically exceeded the required number, especially during weekends and holidays. Better resource planning and a new procedure for weekend and holiday scheduling solved the problem. The total annual savings was estimated at $61,000.

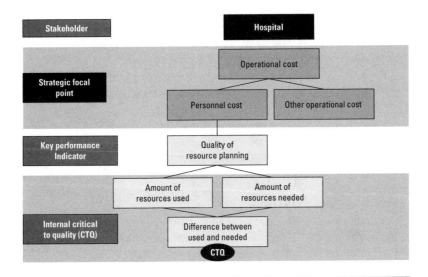

Figure 10   CTQ flowdown for projects aimed at improving resource planning.

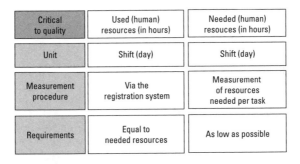

Figure 11   Operational definitions for projects aimed at improving resource planning.

CATEGORY 6.
IMPROVING FACILITY AND
EQUIPMENT USE

In healthcare institutions, available facilities and equipment are often used only partially, even at peak hours. Underused pieces of equipment tie up capital and still require maintenance, driving up operational cost.

The typical CTQs in this category are the number of facilities and equipment available and the use of the facilities and equipment. The difference between available and actually used facilities or equipment is a derived CTQ that indicates the efficiency (see Figure 12). Figure 13 shows generic operational definitions.

Example: In one hospital, an equipment audit found that 22 respirators were available. The specialists wanted to increase this number by four because they had the impression 22 weren't enough.

A Six Sigma project was chartered to look into the number of respirators in use compared to the number of available respirators, hour by hour. The study showed at least 10 spare respirators available at any given time.

With the introduction of a lending system, there was no need to increase the number of respirators, and five respirators were taken off a maintenance

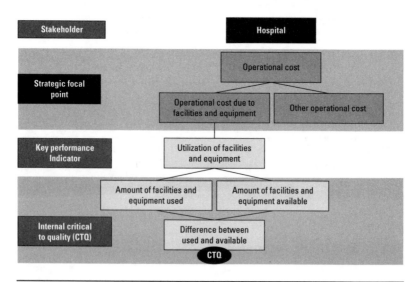

Figure 12 CTQ flowdown for projects aimed at improving the use of facilities and equipment.

Critical to quality	Number in use	Number available
Unit	Time interval (hour)	Time interval (hour)
Measurement procedure	Via measurement form on every equipment or in every facility	Via measurement form on every equipment or in every facility
Requirements	Not applicable	As low as possible

Figure 13 Operational definitions for projects aimed at improving the use of facilities and equipment.

contract. In total, the project saved $39,000 annually in operating costs and produced a capital investment avoidance worth $400,000.

PATTERNS AND COMMONALITIES

Standardization of procedures is a simple but powerful way to make processes more efficient and economical. Similarly, by developing a simple set of problem categories and corresponding standardized templates for the most common Six Sigma projects in healthcare, we can make it easier and more economical to conduct such projects.

Our empirical study of more than 100 Six Sigma healthcare projects shows patterns and commonalities and allows us to draw a number of conclusions:

- The quality, specificity and clarity of the project definition are key factors for success.

- The majority of business improvement projects in healthcare belong to one of the six generic categories of project types we identified.

- These generic project categories have a clear rationale from a business point of view. Most are directly related to drivers of operational cost, while some are related to sales volume and customer satisfaction.

- The project categories are defined broadly enough to allow them to be used throughout a given healthcare organization.

To be effective, healthcare quality improvement projects need to be conducted throughout the entire organization by the people intimately involved with the processes.

The problems in healthcare are too numerous and detailed and typically involve use of local information. These factors make it difficult to hand over these types of problems to specialists, staff functions or consultants. For this reason, healthcare providers—nurses and doctors, in particular—need to assume a leadership role in executing Six Sigma projects.

Recognizing common patterns and structures in the most frequently encountered problems and developing standardized templates for their solutions can significantly lower the barriers to initiating Six Sigma strategies. It also lowers the barriers to having the skills needed and the effort required to successfully complete projects. The results can make a significant contribution to improving the quality and lowering the cost of healthcare.

References

1. J. M. Juran, *Juran on Leadership for Quality,* Free Press, 1989.
2. B. G. Glaser and Anselm Strauss, *The Discovery of Grounded Theory: Strategies for Qualitative Research,* Aldine, 1967.
3. Anselm Strauss and Juliet Corbin, *Basics of Qualitative Research: Grounded Theory Procedures and Techniques,* second edition, Sage, 1998.
4. Mikel Harry, *The Vision of Six Sigma,* Tri Star, 1997.
5. R. G. Cooper, "State-Gate Systems: A New Tool for Managing New Products," *Business Horizons,* Vol. 33, no. 3, 1990, pp. 44–54.
6. Ronald D. Snee and R. W. Hoerl, *Six Sigma: Beyond the Factory Floor,* Pearson Education, 2004.
7. Henk de Koning and Jeroen de Mast, "The CTQ Flowdown As a Conceptual Model of Project Objectives," *International Journal of Quality & Reliability Management,* Vol. 23, no. 7, 2006, pp. 766–787.
8. W. Edwards Deming, *Out of the Crisis,* MIT, 1986.

Bibliography

Barry, Robert, Amy C. Murcko, and Cliff E. Brubaker, *The Six Sigma Book for Healthcare,* Health Administration Press, 2002.

Brady, James E., and Theodore T. Allen, "Six Sigma Literature: A Review and Agenda for Future Research," *Quality and Reliability Engineering International,* Vol. 22, no. 3, 2006, pp. 335–367.

De Koning, Henk, John P. S. Verver, Jaap van den Heuvel, Søren Bisgaard, and Ronald J. M. M. Does, "Lean Six Sigma in Healthcare," *Journal of Healthcare Quality,* Vol. 28, no. 2, 2006, pp. 4–11.

De Mast, Jeroen, Ronald J. M. M. Does, and Henk de Koning, *Lean Six Sigma for Service and Healthcare,* Beaumont Quality Publications, 2006.

George, Michael L., *Lean Six Sigma for Services,* McGraw-Hill, 2003.

Stahl, Robert, Bradley Schultz, and Carolyn Pexton, "Healthcare's Horizon," *Six Sigma Forum Magazine,* Vol. 2, no. 2, 2003, pp. 17–26.

Stock, Greg, "Taking Performance to a Higher Level," *Six Sigma Forum Magazine,* Vol. 1, no. 3, 2002, pp. 23–26.

Van den Heuvel, Jaap, Ronald J. M. M. Does, and M. B. Vermaat, "Six Sigma in a Dutch Hospital: Does It Work in the Nursing Department?" *Quality and Reliability Engineering International,* Vol. 20, no. 5, 2004, pp. 419–426.

Conclusion: Quality Improvement and Innovation

The cases presented in this book provide examples of how teams of nurses, doctors, and others working in healthcare organizations produced managerial innovations that made their institutions more effective in delivering better-quality healthcare at lower cost, using scarce resources, and preventing errors. We need such managerial innovations to match the spectacular medical innovations of the past several decades. Without them, we will not be able to reap the full benefit of the scientific breakthroughs in medical technology, treatments, and medications.

The term *innovation* pertains not only to paradigm-shifting technical advances but also to process innovations and organizational innovations, the type facilitated by Lean Six Sigma. Some of the cases presented can be characterized as process innovations, others as organizational innovations, and some were a bit of both. Some cases involved direct clinical care processes and others were more operational and administrative innovations. Innovations can be either breakthrough or incremental. Both types are important. In some cases an innovation provides more-attractive service features. In other cases the innovation facilitates a cheaper and more efficient process for providing an existing service. As the cases presented have illustrated, the innovations often facilitated better, more attractive features as well as better processes and lower costs. Lean Six Sigma is a managerial program and set of tools for facilitating and managing process and organizational innovation efforts within an institution.

LESSONS LEARNED

Each of the individual cases presented in Parts I and II explains in detail how the teams went about improving quality in their organizations, the problems they encountered, and the results they achieved. Each case has a different message and provides different insights into Lean Six Sigma. Because of the detailed and hands-on nature of the cases, there is much to be learned from reading each of them carefully.

Transcending the specific lessons of each case, taken together they also provide a number of important crosscutting insights, most fundamentally: *it is possible to improve quality while reducing costs.* This is important. There remain many decision makers—clinicians, administrators, and politicians—who are "convinced" it is necessary to make a trade-off between quality and cost. With that mind-set, they may be reluctant to engage in Lean Six Sigma. Fortunately, the cases provide evidence to the contrary.

Beyond the stated objectives of improving quality and reducing cost, the cases collectively also provide a number of additional lessons learned, many of which are universal and just as important as the stated objective of improving quality. We group these into six categories: organization, implementation strategy, methodology, application, culture change, and communication.

Organization

Leadership engagement is critical for successes.

- When appropriately implemented with strong leadership support, Lean Six Sigma can produce significant measurable results. To maintain a sustainable long-term effort, the active engagement of the medical as well as the administrative leadership is a necessity.

- The leadership must provide a broader framework to guide the continued performance improvement efforts and establish priorities and alignment with the strategic direction of the healthcare institution.

- Initial energy and early success is essential. It is, therefore, important to recruit talented and motivated employees for the GB and BB training, especially for the first wave.

- One of the most important aspects of Lean Six Sigma is the system for managing the overall effort. A key component of this system is an effective steering committee composed of representatives from upper management. The steering committee's responsibilities are to:

  - Set up strategic goals for the overall LSS effort

  - Develop general policies and criteria for project selection

  - Develop deployment plans, including training and assistance from consultants

- Allocate resources to support the teams and the general effort

- Select upper-level managers to be Champions

- Conduct regularly scheduled progress reviews

- Provide awards, recognition, and promotions aligned with the goals of Lean Six Sigma

Implementation Strategy

Lean Six Sigma bypasses lengthy preparations typical of other quality management approaches and instead aims for measurable and relevant results within the first six months.

- It is better to introduce innovations incrementally in support of specific organizational goals. The LSS efforts should start in a few organizational units where management is positively inclined to the ideas of Lean Six Sigma. Once success has been demonstrated, the leadership should roll out the effort to additional units. The initial success will encourage departmental management to extend and support the program.

- Unlike other approaches to quality management, it is not necessary to engage in time-consuming and costly organizationwide assessments before getting started with Lean Six Sigma. Upper management typically knows well about a number of major quality problems that can serve as projects for the initial rollout of Lean Six Sigma. For those initial projects, aim directly at accomplishing measurable results quickly. An assessment may be useful later, for example, a year into implementing Lean Six Sigma in an organization.

- It is important to select projects that will produce strategically meaningful results. The first projects should be selected carefully so they have a high probability of success. The focus should be on achieving *specific, measurable, operational* improvements within a few months.

- Quick, tangible results will boost the morale of the employees and build confidence.

- The teams learn by doing the projects. Allow them to make mistakes while they learn the LSS methodology. However, teams should be held accountable for DMAIC methodology and their schedule. As the teams develop skills in LSS methodology, they will be able to tackle more difficult and larger-scope problems.

- Those closest to a process are often in the best position to improve a process. Lean Six Sigma empowers people closest to and most familiar with a process to develop and implement appropriate solutions.

- Nurses are often those with the most intimate knowledge of processes that involve patient care. It is, therefore, particularly important to have nurses trained as GBs and BBs so they become empowered to work on improvement and master the tools and methodology of Lean Six Sigma.

Methodology

Quality improvement is like detective work, with team members working together to discover the underlying causes of problems.

- The DMAIC discipline helps teams structure their approach to problem solving. It is important to strictly follow the DMAIC cycle and have well-structured project reviews between each phase. It is the Champion's responsibility to conduct the reviews.

- The essence of Lean Six Sigma is decision making based on fact, data, and deliberate analysis.

- The basic tools of quality improvement—flowcharts (or process maps), cause-and-effect diagrams, Pareto charts, control charts, time series plots, box plots, and other simple graphical methods— are the most used, most powerful, and most important tools. When combined with common sense, these tools are often all that is necessary. It is unusual to need more-complex statistical methodologies.

- It is not the particular solutions that are generalizable to other settings and other institutions. It is the methodology for developing the solutions—a scientific approach to problem solving—that is the universal ingredient.

- Causes for quality problems generally can be categorized as either due to special causes or to systems causes. Problems resulting from special causes are the responsibility of the individual operating the process to fix. Problems attributable to systems causes are the responsibility of management to fix. The general rule of thumb is that 80 percent of all quality problems are due to systems causes.

- It is important for the quality detectives to go beyond the obvious and look deeper for root causes of problems. For example, errors committed by employees are often due to misunderstanding of guidelines, instructions, and procedures. If so, they are due to systems causes. In such case, the right response is not to blame the individual, but for management to institute managerial changes such as additional or revised training, standard procedures, and close supervision.

- In healthcare, the introduction of, careful instruction in, and consistent use of standard procedures by all involved in particular processes go a long way to reduce errors and variability.

Application

Lean Six Sigma applies to improving clinical, managerial, and administrative quality.

- Lean Six Sigma applies in a wide variety of settings: within individual departments, across traditional departmental barriers, within rural hospitals, within large teaching facilities, and across multi-hospital systems.

- Lean Six Sigma is no longer just about reducing defects. It applies to addressing a wide variety of operational and process problems including waste and inefficiency. The drive should be to develop systems that provide better value.

- Although sporadic quality problems need, and typically get, immediate attention, we ought to concentrate on working on chronic quality problems and prevention.

Culture Change

A frontal attack on culture change rarely works.

- It is more effective to focus on achieving operational results. Culture change will follow naturally.

- Culture change occurs when employees modify their behavior, how they solve problems, and how they cooperate when solving problems. Behavior is best modeled, not lectured about. The disciplined Lean Six Sigma way of solving problems represents a behavioral change. The individual employee's change of behavior is what changes an organization's culture.

- Successful programs focused on changing behavior rely on the active involvement and participation of the employees. The organization's members—the GBs, the BBs, the LSS team members, and the Champions—are the change agents, not external consultants. With Lean Six Sigma, the employees drive the operational and behavioral changes that eventually result in culture change.

- The data-driven approach reduces emotional reactions, unnecessary politics, and resistance to change.

- Before introducing Lean Six Sigma, medical personnel are sometimes reluctant to make changes that contradict their intuition and previous work habits. Once they begin to use the data-driven DMAIC process, they are more easily persuaded to confront old habits with data and fact, make appropriate changes, and check the effects against new data.

- After introducing Lean Six Sigma, management and staff typically develop a positive attitude toward data-driven decision making, recognize the importance of using relevant metrics in making decisions, and approach operational problems in a more rigorous, data-driven manner.

- When quality and patient satisfaction are improved, employees become happier and more productive. Job satisfaction and employee morale are typically improved as a by-product of the LSS process.

Communication

Successful LSS projects often help develop stronger partnerships within and between departments.

- Lean Six Sigma helps break down barriers between departments and improve interdepartmental communication. People who had never before worked together typically meet and collaboratively address common problems. The operational data collected, shared, and analyzed via the DMAIC problem-solving process is the catalyst for the better communication. This improvement can strengthen routine interdepartmental operations and provide a foundation for constructive problem solving in the future.

- Different professional groups within healthcare institutions are sometimes at odds because of a lack of proper communication, different perspectives, or local pressures. With the LSS methodology and the use of data, they begin see each other as mutual customers.

SUCCESS AND FAILURE

The cases presented in this book are almost all success stories. There is obviously a selection bias in our collection of cases; few would write a paper about an unsuccessful implementation of Lean Six Sigma. However, it would be naive to think that LSS programs always work out. Any experienced consultant has clearly seen a number of failures. Many of us have also thought about why failure occurs. The consensus is that a major reason for failure is lack of direct involvement by upper management in the LSS effort. It is not enough for upper management to say that it supports Lean Six Sigma. It must take its role very seriously and get involved, show genuine leadership by serving on the Lean Six Sigma steering committee, and provide adequate resources for the effort; see Snee and Hoerl (2003) for further discussion.

Beyond lack of serious top management involvement, there are a number of additional reasons the Lean Six Sigma effort may not work so well. We mention a few we have experienced in the past:

- Some senior departmental managers were skeptical of Lean Six Sigma and worked against the effort in their departments. If someone wants to "prove" that something does not work, it is very easy to do so.

- Champions did not take the role seriously, did not hold teams to their schedule, did not perform rigorous progress reviews between each of the DMAIC phases, and did not stop projects from going forward when they did not meet stated goals.

- People selected for the GB and BB training were not necessarily top talent and interested in the effort.

- GBs and BBs were not provided sufficient time off from their regular jobs to work on projects and not provided with adequate resources.

- Projects were poorly selected and not of sufficient strategic importance for the organization.

- Project goals and objectives were vague and not stated in results-oriented terms; the schedule was not firm and projects not scoped to achieve tangible results within a few months.

To further understand why quality initiatives sometimes fail, Juran (1989) provides an interesting comparison of the delegation of tasks between a traditional managerial function, for example finance, and that of the typical quality function within an organization. His analysis, with some modifications, is reproduced here as Table C.1. From the table it is easy to see that

Table C.1 Contrast in delegation of traditional managerial tasks and responsibilities compared to those typical for many quality management efforts. Quality management efforts would have a better chance of success if they were delegated more firmly as in the center column (traditional management tasks).

Elements of delegation	Delegation of traditional management tasks	Typical delegation of quality management tasks
Goals	Clear: schedules, budgets, specifications	Vague: slogans—quality has top priority; do it right the first time
Responsibility	Clear: specific as to departments, individuals	Vague: general, nonspecific
Resources	Provided as part of budgeting and planning	Not provided; not a part of budgeting and planning
Training	Oriented toward job performance	Oriented to quality awareness
Measures of performance	In place: reports on results versus goals	Not provided
Reviews	Regularly scheduled; personal reviews by upper managers	Not provided
Rewards	Keyed to performance against goals	Not provided

Adapted from Juran (1989): 76.

the quality function, if the tasks and responsibilities are delegated as indicated, is set up to fail.

WHERE DO WE GO FROM HERE?

Healthcare is at a crossroads. We need initiatives and solutions at the political and the policy levels. Many innovations can only occur if we fundamentally restructure the way we deliver, administrate, and pay for healthcare. However, we need not wait for political solutions to make progress. Healthcare professionals—doctors, nurses, and administrators—can immediately assume leadership within their own institutions by applying quality management principles and proven approaches to quality improvement. They can start quality improvement programs now—even while the public debate continues. Our cases show how.

Our case studies have, in the main, provided better solutions within existing healthcare delivery systems. We should continue such efforts. There are significant gains to be made with great benefit to patients and healthcare professionals alike. The LSS methodology will always be helpful in facilitating such improvements regardless of the restructuring of the healthcare system that will be implemented at the political level in the coming years.

As we look to the future, we need to consider broadening Lean Six Sigma efforts and look for whole new transformative structures for delivering better patient health and better value for patients. For example, in the case of chronic diseases, rather than focusing on individual incidents and treatments, we should consider the whole cycle of care. Today too many patients end up in the emergency room when they would be much better served, at much lower cost, in less expensive health services facilities. For the elderly we can design and develop comprehensive systems to manage their care, often at a much lower cost. In general, we should develop integrated systems that focus on prevention and ultimately on improving the quality of life. Lean Six Sigma can help to develop and refine such systems.

Another application area for Lean Six Sigma is the management of health insurance and health administration in general. So far these areas have not been the subject of Lean Six Sigma, but we predict that there are rich opportunities here for achieving better efficiency and higher quality.

The cases presented in this book represent the work of pioneers from a variety of healthcare institutions willing to take the risk and engage in experiments to improve the quality of their services. They adopted an approach to quality management in healthcare based on discovering practical ways to actively improve the quality of care in their institutions rather than mechanical compliance with standards and external mandates, as is too often the case. These pioneers have demonstrated for all of us that this results-oriented, pragmatic approach to quality improvement based on the ideas of Lean Six Sigma works in the healthcare context and is extremely effective. It is our hope that this book will provide guidance and be an inspiration to others to do likewise.

References

Juran, J. M. *Juran on Leadership for Quality.* New York: The Free Press, 1989.
Snee, R. D., and R. W. Hoerl. *Leading Six Sigma.* Upper Saddle River, NJ: FT Prentice Hall, 2003.

About the Editor

Dr. Søren Bisgaard is the Eugene M. Isenberg professor of integrative studies at the University of Massachusetts Amherst and professor of business and industrial statistics at the department of economics, University of Amsterdam. He is an internationally recognized consultant in Six Sigma quality management and applied statistics. His areas of specialty are technology management and entrepreneurship, including quality management, operations management, design of experiments, process improvement and control, statistics, economics, innovation, and product design. For the past 25 years he has consulted extensively for leading U.S., European, and Asian companies such as Hewlett-Packard, Bell Labs, General Motors, Ford, DaimlerChrysler, S. C. Johnson, Mercury Marine, Philips, and Samsung. Dr. Bisgaard holds degrees in industrial and manufacturing engineering from Denmark, and MS and PhD degrees in statistics from the University of Wisconsin–Madison. Prior to his current academic appointments he has held positions as professor and director of the department for quality management and technology at the University of St. Gallen, Switzerland, and professor of industrial engineering at the University of Wisconsin–Madison. While at the University of Wisconsin, he worked with George Box and William G. Hunter creating and managing the internationally recognized Center for Quality and Productivity Improvement and was its director from 1991 to 1999. Professor Bisgaard is a fellow of the American Society for Quality (ASQ) and of the American Statistical Association, and author of more than 120 publications on statistics, design of experiments and quality management. He has received numerous awards, including ASQ's Shewhart Medal, the Ott Award, the Wilcoxon Prize, the Shewell Award, and the Brumbaugh Award. Professor Bisgaard has taught short courses and workshops throughout the United States, Europe, and Asia, is a frequent keynote speaker at international conferences, is the founding chair of the European Network for Business and Industrial Statistics (ENBIS), serves on the editorial board of *Journal of Quality Technology*, *Quality Engineering*, and *Applied Statistics*, and is on the management board of *Technometrics*.

Index

Belong to the Quality Community!

Established in 1946, ASQ is a global community of quality experts in all fields and industries. ASQ is dedicated to the promotion and advancement of quality tools, principles, and practices in the workplace and in the community.

The Society also serves as an advocate for quality. Its members have informed and advised the U.S. Congress, government agencies, state legislatures, and other groups and individuals worldwide on quality-related topics.

Vision

By making quality a global priority, an organizational imperative, and a personal ethic, ASQ becomes the community of choice for everyone who seeks quality technology, concepts, or tools to improve themselves and their world.

ASQ is...

- More than 90,000 individuals and 700 companies in more than 100 countries
- The world's largest organization dedicated to promoting quality
- A community of professionals striving to bring quality to their work and their lives
- The administrator of the Malcolm Baldrige National Quality Award
- A supporter of quality in all sectors including manufacturing, service, healthcare, government, and education
- YOU

ASQ

Visit www.asq.org for more information.

ASQ Membership

Research shows that people who join associations experience increased job satisfaction, earn more, and are generally happier*. ASQ membership can help you achieve this while providing the tools you need to be successful in your industry and to distinguish yourself from your competition. So why wouldn't you want to be a part of ASQ?

Networking

Have the opportunity to meet, communicate, and collaborate with your peers within the quality community through conferences and local ASQ section meetings, ASQ forums or divisions, ASQ Communities of Quality discussion boards, and more.

Professional Development

Access a wide variety of professional development tools such as books, training, and certifications at a discounted price. Also, ASQ certifications and the ASQ Career Center help enhance your quality knowledge and take your career to the next level.

Solutions

Find answers to all your quality problems, big and small, with ASQ's Knowledge Center, mentoring program, various e-newsletters, *Quality Progress* magazine, and industry-specific products.

Access to Information

Learn classic and current quality principles and theories in ASQ's Quality Information Center (QIC), *ASQ Weekly* e-newsletter, and product offerings.

Advocacy Programs

ASQ helps create a better community, government, and world through initiatives that include social responsibility, Washington advocacy, and Community Good Works.

Visit www.asq.org/membership for more information on ASQ membership.

*2008, The William E. Smith Institute for Association Research